The Best Web Sites for Teachers

Fourth Edition

Richard M. Sharp
Vicki F. Sharp
Martin G. Levine

SCHOOL OF EDUCATION
CURRICULUM LABORATORY
UM-DEARBORN

©2001 The International Society for Technology in Education, Fourth Edition

The Best Web Sites for Teachers
Richard M. Sharp
Vicki F. Sharp
Martin G. Levine

Director of Publishing
Jean Marie Hall

Acquisitions Editors
Anita Best
Matthew Manweller

Book Publishing Project Manager
Tracy Cozzens

Special Projects Manager
Diannah Anavir

Administrative Assistant
Pam Calegari

Copy Editor
Steve Cozzens

Cover Design
Sue Roberts

Layout and Production
Tracy Cozzens

Library of Congress Card Number: 00-111189

The International Society for Technology in Education (ISTE)
480 Charnelton Street
Eugene, OR 97401-2626
Order Desk: 800.336.5191
Order Fax: 541.302.3778
Customer Service: orders@iste.org
Books and Courseware: books@iste.org
World Wide Web: www.iste.org

Fourth Edition
ISBN 1-56484-169-3

About ISTE

The International Society for Technology in Education (ISTE) is a nonprofit professional organization with a worldwide membership of leaders in educational technology. We are dedicated to promoting appropriate uses of information technology to support and improve learning, teaching, and administration in K–12 education and teacher education. As part of that mission, ISTE provides high-quality and timely information, services, and materials, such as this book.

The ISTE Publishing Department works with experienced educators to develop and produce classroom-tested books and courseware. We look for content that emphasizes the use of technology where it can make a difference—making the teacher's job easier; saving time; motivating students; helping students who have unique learning styles, abilities, or backgrounds; and creating learning environments that would be impossible without technology. We believe technology can improve the effectiveness of teaching while making learning exciting and fun.

Every manuscript and product we select for publication is peer reviewed and professionally edited. While we take pride in our publications, we also recognize the difficulties of maintaining quality while keeping on top of the latest technologies and research. Please let us know what products you would find helpful. We value your feedback on this book and other ISTE products. E-mail us at books@iste.org.

ISTE is home of the National Educational Technology Standards (NETS) Project and the National Center for Preparing Tomorrow's Teachers to Use Technology (NCPT³). To learn more about NETS or request a print catalog, visit our Web site at **www.iste.org**, which provides:

- Current educational technology standards for K–12 student and teacher education

- A bookstore with online ordering and membership discount options

- *Learning & Leading with Technology* magazine

- *ISTE Update,* membership newsletter

- Teacher resources

- Discussion groups

- Professional development services, including national conference information

- Research projects

- Member services

About the Authors

Dr. Richard M. Sharp, Professor of Elementary Education at California State University, Northridge, is the author of numerous books and articles on topics related to mathematics. His other titles published by the International Society for Technology in Education include *The Best Web Sites for Teachers, First, Second and Third Editions* (1996, 1998, 1999) and *The Best Math and Science Web Sites for Teachers* (1997). He has also authored *WebDoctor* (Quality Medical Book—St. Martin Distributor, 1998), *Scribble Scrabble and Other Ready-in-a-Minute Math Games* (McGraw-Hill, 1995), and *The Sneaky Square and Other Math Activities* (McGraw-Hill, 1996). He serves as a computer consultant and trainer for software publishers and school districts in Southern California. He currently writes a medical column for Health Scout. He has also coauthored a Web page titled Web Sites and Resources for Teachers, which covers all curriculum areas (http://www.sitesforteachers.com).

Dr. Vicki F. Sharp, Professor of Elementary Education at California State University, Northridge, is the author of numerous books and articles on topics related to the use of computers in education. Her other titles published by the International Society for Technology in Education include *PowerPoint 98 In One Hour—Macintosh* (1999), *PowerPoint 97 In One Hour—Windows* (1999), *Best Web Sites for Teachers, First, Second, and Third Editions* (1996, 1998, 1999), *HyperStudio 3.2 In One Hour—Windows* (1998), *HyperStudio 3.2 In One Hour—Macintosh* (1997), *Netscape Navigator 3.0 In One Hour* (1997), *The Best Math and Science Web Sites for Teachers* (1997). She has also authored *WebDoctor* (Quality Medical Book—St. Martin Distributor, 1998), *Computer Education for Teachers, Third Edition* (McGraw-Hill, 1999), *Make it with Office, Make it with Inspiration* (Visions Technology in Education, 1999, 2000), *Internet Guide for Education* (Wadsworth, 1996), and *Scribble Scrabble and Other Ready-in-a-Minute Math Games* (McGraw-Hill, 1995). She frequently writes about children's software for magazines, and serves as a computer consultant and trainer for software publishers and school districts in Southern California. With her husband Dr. Richard M. Sharp, she maintains a Web site covering all curriculum areas (http://www.sitesforteachers.com/).

Dr. Martin G. Levine teaches courses in methods of teaching social studies, ESL, and bilingual education at California State University, Northridge. Dr. Levine holds the Bilingual Certificate of Competence and the General Secondary Credential awarded by the State of California. He has taught social studies and English at the secondary level and has published articles in social studies and foreign language journals for teachers. He has coauthored the International Society for Technology in Education titles *The Best Web Sites for Teachers First, Second, and Third Editions* (1996, 1998, 1999) and *The Best Math and Science Web Sites for Teachers* (1997). He has also authored numerous Web pages covering such topics as foreign language instruction, ESL, and social studies. The type of content and URLs for these pages are: Lesson Plans and Resources for ESL and Bilingual Teachers (http://www.csun.edu/~hcedu013/eslindex.html), Foreign Language Study Abroad (http://www.csun.edu/~hcedu013/LanguageAbroad.html), and Lesson Plans and Resources for Social Studies Teachers (http://www.csun.edu/~hcedu013/index.html).

Acknowledgments

We wish to thank Anita McAnear, Jean Hall, Tracy Cozzens, Ron Renchler, and Christy McMannis for their excellent editorial work, advice, and invaluable assistance and direction. Thanks to Judi Mathis Johnson at ISTE and Susan Dahl at the Fermi National Accelerator Laboratory Lederman Science Center-IRC for their development work on the ISTE forms for evaluating new and recommended Web sites. Thanks also goes to Tracy Cozzens for her competence and diligence in preparing this book for publication.

Thanks to David Gartner, Public Relations Manager of Equilibrium, for DeBabelizer, a real time-saver. DeBabelizer was used to batch produce the screenshots and enhance the images. You can reach Equilibrium by phone at 415.332.4343 or on the Web at http://www.equilibrium.com.

Richard and Vicki Sharp offer a very special thanks to their son David *(at left)* for his encouragement.

This book is dedicated to Vicki Sharp's parents, Bobbie E. Friedman and the late Paul J. Friedman.

Richard M. Sharp
Vicki F. Sharp
Martin G. Levine
California State University, Northridge
October 2000

Contents

Introduction

New to the Fourth Edition

The Fourth Edition of *The Best Web Sites for Teachers* incorporates additions and changes to the Third Edition resulting from changes on the World Wide Web. Included are:

- More sites offering lesson plans

- From 25% to 30% new sites described

- Deletion of sites no longer in existence

- Updated links for all sites

- A Revised Getting Started section for Internet Explorer and Netscape Communicator

The Internet and the World Wide Web: What Are They?

The terms *Internet* and *World Wide Web* permeate every facet of our lives. Everywhere we travel, we hear people talking about worldwide communication using the Internet. We see it in print, in magazines and newspapers, and hear it discussed on television, on talk radio, and in educational circles.

The Internet is a huge, worldwide network of connected computer networks with no single master control-center or authority. The Internet was created in 1969 for military research purposes by the U.S. Department of Defense. The Defense Department was concerned with ensuring mass communication of information while providing maximum security. Although the Internet has existed for a long time, until recently it has been difficult for the general public to access. Because of this, only scientists and academics used it. It wasn't until 1989 with the development of the World Wide Web that the general public began heavily using the Internet.

The World Wide Web is an easy way to navigate the Internet. The Web incorporates text, graphics, and sounds in electronic documents called *home pages* or *Web sites*. Each home page or Web site has its own unique URL, or address. (URL stands for Uniform Resource Locator.)

Certain items on Web pages are underlined. These underlined items are called *links*. The World Wide Web gets its name from these links because they are like threads in a spider's web. By clicking the link with the mouse, you can jump from one page on the Web to another, be it a page on the same computer or a page on another computer on the other side of the world. One document is linked to another, which is linked to another, and so on.

What's on the World Wide Web for Teachers?

There are thousands of useful Web sites for teachers that take advantage of the Web's multimedia capabilities. You can visit a museum, take a lesson in a foreign language, play a math game, explore the human brain, read interactive stories, participate in online polls and discussion groups, listen to music, and download lesson plans.

How Can I Find Things on the World Wide Web?

The World Wide Web provides you with tools to search for resources. These search tools bear names such as Inference Find, Google.com, HotBot.com, AltaVista, Yahoo!, Deja News, Excite, Ask Jeeves, Snap, About.com, Looksmart.com. (See Appendix 2 for Web site information on various search tools.) You enter keywords to find lists of sites that may contain the information you are looking for. Another way to find information on the Web is to know the address (the URL) for a site. All Web URLs start with http://. For example, to connect to the homepage ISTE's National Educational Technology Standards, you would type http://cnets.iste.org/.

How Do I Access the World Wide Web?

To access the Web, you need a connection to the Internet, which you can get through a commercial Internet Service Provider (ISP). Two popular ones are America Online (800-827-6364), and Earthlink (800-395-8410). Online service providers usually charge less than $20 per month for unlimited Internet access. If you already have access to the Internet, you can find a list of ISPs using *The List* at http://thelist.internet.com/.

Another place to find information is in your Yellow Pages or from a local computer user group.

What Kind of Computer Hardware and Software Do I Need?

To access the Web effectively, you need a computer running Windows with at least a Pentium I processor and 64 MB (megabytes) of RAM, or a Macintosh computer running System 7.0 or higher with at least 64 MB of memory. You will also need a modem. If possible, use a modem with a transfer speed of 56K. A 28.8-bps modem will work, but it will operate at a much slower speed.

What Is the Purpose of This Book?

We, the authors, have searched the Internet and World Wide Web and identified more than 700 sites across the K–12 curriculum that we feel will benefit busy teachers who may not have time to carry out lengthy searches themselves. We believe that this collection of sites will provide teachers with a good starting place for Internet exploration on their own. Be forewarned that Internet resources come and go. There is no guarantee that all of the sites included in this book will be accessible when you try to open them. You might find that the problem is temporary or that the resource simply moved to a different address. Or the site may have been removed. If your initial effort to visit a specific Web site fails, try again later. Because Web sites are frequently redesigned to take advantage of the latest developments in Web technology, when you access a site you may find that what you see on your monitor is different from the graphic display provided in this book.

How Is This Book Organized?

The Web sites in this book are organized alphabetically by the following K–12 subject areas: art, bilingual education, drama, English as a second language, foreign language, health education/physical education, journalism, language arts, math, multicultural, multiple subjects, music, science, social studies, special education, and vocational/technical education. Within each subject area, the sites are organized into at least one of three categories: lesson plans, other resources, and exhibits and museums.

In addition, **Appendix 1** describes Web sites for discussion groups, called *newsgroups*, that allow teachers to read and post messages. These groups are similar to electronic bulletin boards. Appendix 1 also describes mailing lists, or *listservs*, through which teachers can subscribe to electronic newsletters. **Appendix 2** lists Web sites for information on search tools. **Appendix 3** provides sample forms for evaluating recommended and new Web sites. The Web sites mentioned in this book are indexed both alphabetically by title and alphabetically by title within each subject area.

What's Included in the Descriptions of Sites?

The sites described for each subject area may include a wide range of material—lesson plans and pictures that can be printed, online multimedia presentations for students, interactive games, weekly brain teasers, searchable activities, databases for teachers, contests, penpal opportunities, forms, downloadable graphics, videos, and many other resources that can enrich the K–12 curriculum. The descriptions of the sites usually indicate whether the sites are for teachers or students, as well as the grade levels for which the site material is intended.

What Were the Criteria for Selecting the Sites?

Because anyone with access to the Web can easily establish a Web site, many so-called educational Web sites contain little useful information, even though they may be visually appealing. Furthermore, many sites with good information contain graphics that take too long to download to your computer and therefore tax the attention span of both adults and students who are accustomed to fast-paced forms of media. Many sites are poorly constructed with hard-to-read screens, inactive or missing links, and distracting graphics. In selecting sites to include in this book, we considered how appropriate, relevant, and useful the sites would be for teaching and enhancing the K–12 curriculum. We have selected sites that, in general, fulfill the following criteria:

🌍 The site contains appropriate, relevant, and timely information.

🌍 The site is organized effectively on a stable Internet location with good connectivity so that teachers and students can easily find the information they are seeking.

🌍 The site can be downloaded in a reasonable period of time.

🌍 The site is updated regularly.

🌍 The site is an award winner that has been cited for having valuable, authoritative, and reliable information.

The two evaluation forms in Appendix 3 offer criteria to help you evaluate educational Web sites on your own. The first form, **Educational Web Sites Recommended by Others**, will help you evaluate sites described in this book for use in your own classroom. The second form, **Educational Web Sites You Discover**, will help you evaluate new sites you encounter in your Web travels.

Keep Us Up to Date

We hope that this book will enrich your Webbing experience and translate into more productive time on the Internet. If you have comments or wish to add some of your favorite Web sites to the next edition, please let us know. E-mail us at vicki.sharp@csun.edu.

Getting Started With Your Browser

To take advantage of the Web, you need a software program called a *browser*. All Web pages displayed in this book can be opened using either Microsoft Internet Explorer or Netscape Communicator. They both work in a similar way, although the display of the home page on your monitor may look different. The following instructions tell you how to enter a URL to display a home page.

Netscape Communicator

After you launch Netscape Navigator, you will see a toolbar at the top of its window. The toolbar has commands such as **Print**, **Home**, and **Back**.

Now follow these steps.

1. If you are using Netscape Communicator 4.5, from the **File** menu, point to **Open** then choose **Location in Navigator** (⌘-O)

*Note: For Netscape 3.0, click **Open** on the toolbar.*

2. Type the following URL in the Location dialog box: http://www.csun.edu/ ~vceed009/

3. Click the **Open** button.

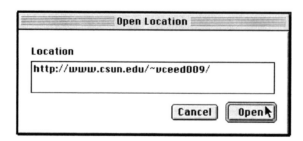

Internet Explorer

After launching Internet Explorer, you will see a toolbar with commands such as **Stop**, **Back**, and **Forward**.

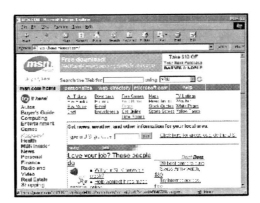

Now follow these steps.

1. From the **File** menu, click **Open** (Ctrl + O).

2. Type the following URL in the Open dialog box: http://www.csun.edu/ ~vceed009/

3. Click the **OK** button.

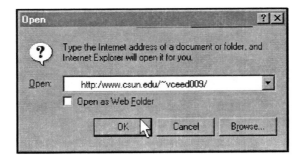

Netscape Communicator and Internet Explorer

4. After a few seconds, the home page corresponding to the URL will appear.

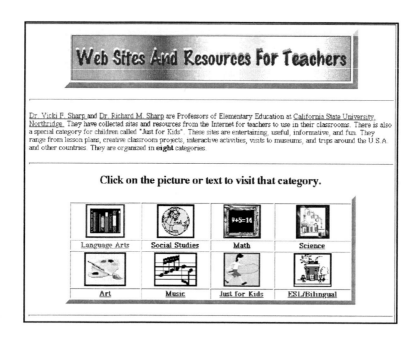

5. Wait until the page is fully loaded on your screen. You will see the word *Done* or the words *Document: Done* at the bottom of the screen.

6. You are now ready to explore *links*, or connections, to other Web pages. Links are words that are underlined or displayed in a different color, or are pictures that have a colored border around them. (In the descriptions of Web sites in this book, you are sometimes directed to navigate through specific links, which appear as capitalized words, e.g., Table of Contents.)

7. Click an underlined word link, shown in this illustration:

or a picture link, shown in this one:

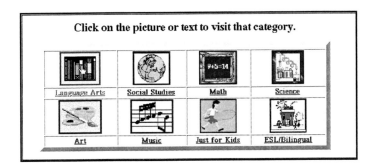

Note: When the mouse passes over a live link, the pointer (or arrow) becomes a hand.

Tips for Netscape Communicator and Internet Explorer Users

Other browsers work similarly to Netscape Communicator and Internet Explorer, so these tips apply to those browsers as well.

- When you type a URL in the **Location** or **Open** box, you can omit the http:// part of the URL; it will still work.

- Use the **Back** button to return to the previous site or page.

- If you cannot open a site with a given URL, use a search tool, such as Infoseek, Yahoo!, Ask Jeeves, Excite, Snap.com, About.com, Infind.com, Magellan, or AltaVista. In the search box, type the title of the site exactly as it appears (not its URL). The search tool might pick up the new URL for the title entered. The All-in-One Search Page (see Appendix 2) features a compilation of search tools which can help you find things on the Internet. The URL is **www.allonesearch.com/**.

- When using a search engine, you can narrow your search and avoid thousands of unnecessary hits. For example, when using Yahoo!, click the **Options** button and try using an "exact phrase" match. In Yahoo! you can also scroll to the bottom of the page and click other search engines that are listed.

- When searching, avoid generic or commonly used words. For example, a search for "baseball" might be too general and will deliver a tremendous number of matches. A search for "1970 World Series" is much more exact. The best searches use terms, words, or phrases that correspond to words, terms, or phrases in the documents you want to find.

- Most search engines let you link your search terms with words such as "and," "or," or "minus" (-), as well as search for phrases by placing the words in quotation marks. For example, you might search for "Stan Musial and World Series," which would give you information on both topics. If you replace "and" with "or," the search would be directed to identify one topic or the other. If you replace the "and" with the minus sign (no spaces), the engine will find pages that contain references to Stan Musial but not the World Series. These connectors vary with each search engine. Check your search engine's help page for more tips.

   For an excellent tutorial on searching, visit the following link: **www.britannica.com/bcom/search/tips/**.

- When you find a site you like, bookmark it so that you don't have to enter the URL for the site again.

➡ From Netscape Communicator's **Bookmarks** menu, select **Add Bookmark**. The site will now be listed under the **Bookmarks** menu, and Netscape Communicator will take you to the site whenever you select it.

➡ From Internet Explorer's **Favorites** menu, select **Add to Favorites**. Type the name for the site or use the name supplied. Click the OK button. The site will now be listed under the Favorites List, and Internet Explorer will take you to the site whenever you select it.

⊕ The print size on a page may be too small for easy reading. However, most browsers let you change the size of the words as displayed on the screen.

➡ In Netscape Communicator 4.5, from the **Edit** menu, choose **Preferences**. In the Preferences dialog box, from the Category scroll list, choose **Fonts** under **Appearance**. Choose a different size or type of font.

*Note: Netscape 3.0 uses the menu path **General Preferences—Fonts**.*

➡ In Internet Explorer, go to the **View** menu, point to **Text Size**, and then choose a larger or smaller font for the text on that page.

⊕ If you just print the information from the site, you might get pages you don't need. To avoid this, go to **Print Preview** and determine how many pages you need. Now specify in the Print dialog box which pages you want to print. (If your browser does not have Print Preview, arbitrarily set a fixed number of pages in the Print dialog box.

⊕ Instead of printing pages, you can save them with the **Save As** feature in your browser. You have a choice of **Source** or **Text**. If you select Text, the pages will have no colors or formatting and can be opened with your word processor. If you select Source, the document is saved as an HTML document with color and formatting. The graphics must be saved separately.

➡ In Netscape Communicator, press the mouse button while on a graphic. When the dialog box pops up, select **Save this image as**.

➡ In Internet Explorer, right-click the graphic. Then click **Save Picture As** on the short menu that appears.

Be sure to use the contact information on the Web page to request permission to use a graphic, and credit the source if you use it. Look for Web sites that give users permission to use the graphics for noncommercial purposes.

⊕ You can search long Web pages for a specific word or words.

➡ In Netscape Communicator, press Command-F (⌘-F) on your keyboard. Type the word in the dialog box. Then click **Find** in the dialog box, or press Return on your keyboard. The word will appear highlighted.

➡ In Internet Explorer, press Control + F (Ctrl + F) on your keyboard in the dialog box that appears, type the word, and then click **Find Next**. The word will appear highlighted.

Tips for Finding Inaccessible URLs

Be forewarned that Internet resources come and go with amazing speed. We cannot guarantee that all of the sites included in this book will be accessible when you try to open them. You might find messages such as: "404 Not Found" or "No DNS entry exists for this server." Here are some tips to help you locate the site when you receive these types of messages.

⊕ Try opening the site again a few seconds later. Sometimes that works because the Internet computer serving the documents may be down temporarily or it may be so busy that you can't get in at the moment. Occasionally, the problem may be caused by your Internet Service Provider or commercial online service, which may be having problems with its Internet lines.

☽ If you have waited more than 50 seconds and think that the site should have loaded by then, click the **Stop** button. Then click **Reload**.

☽ Make sure you have spelled the URL exactly as it is printed in this book, using upper- and lowercase letters where appropriate. The Web is case sensitive, so "Csun" is not the same as "csun."

☽ If suddenly your sites are not loading, you may have to go offline and reboot your system.

☽ To load a site faster, turn off the graphics and sound options on your browser. Although graphics and audio files are great, they take forever to load. In most instances, you can make text-only loading your browser's default setting. After seeing the site, you can turn on those options and return to examine the site again.

☽ If you can't find a site, you can sometimes physically modify your URL to get the page you desire. For example, when you try to dial up the Medical Matrix: Patient Education page at www.medmatrix.org/SPages/ Patient_Education_and_Support.stm, you may get an error message. Try deleting the final segment "Patient_Education_and_Support.stm" and press Return or Enter. Continue removing segments from the URL up to the forward slashes until it works. For this example, the URL www.medmatrix.org/ will work.

☽ Because the Web is always changing, sites switch servers, change their names, or just disappear forever. In many cases the old location will point you to the site's new location. If this is not the case, try using the company's name or product names in the URL. For instance, to find information about Apple Computing, type www.apple.com/. If this procedure doesn't work, go to a search engine and type Apple Computing.

☽ Many sites maintain numerous servers to accommodate high volume. Most Web masters limit the number of users to make sure the servers don't become overloaded. To overcome this difficulty, try another server. For example Netscape Communicator numbers its servers. If you can't access ftp://ftp3.netscape.com/, try ftp://ftp4.netscape.com/, and so forth.

☽ Finally, instead of looking through one search engine at a time, try using the search engine MetaCrawler, which allows you to search several engines at the same time. MetaCrawler can be found at **www.metacrawler.com**. Another choice is Infind.com, which can be found at **www.infind.com**.

*Note: The "Best Search Tools" is a guide that describes and compares information on all the major search engines. Its URL is: **http://infopeople.org/src/schools.htm**.*

Art

AskERIC Lesson Plans

http://ericir.syr.edu/Virtual/Lessons/Arts/Art_Activities/

AskERIC Lesson Plans provides more than 25 lesson plans for students in grades K-12.

Art/Crafts for Kids

http://kidsartscrafts.about.com/kids/kidsartscrafts/

Art/Crafts for Kids contains a treasury of lesson plans, art activities, crafts, art history, museums, galleries, drawing, cartooning, visual arts, multicultural, architecture, crafty recipes, and much more.

Art Projects

http://www.bway.net/~starlite/projects.htm

Art Projects, by Barbara Sonek, contains a collection of projects to do in K-12 classrooms.

The Art Room

http://www.arts.ufl.edu/art/rt_room/index.html

The Art Room features a variety of classroom projects for grades 3-12 in the Doorway section. This section also includes other useful art activities, including the Artifacts Center.

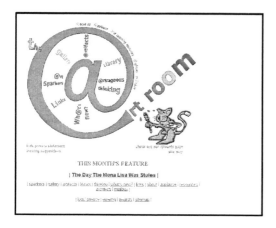

Art Takes Time

http://members.aol.com/TWard64340/Index.htm

Art Takes Time, created by Tabitha Ward for elementary school students, contains a collection of lesson plans for various artistic movements from cave art to modern art.

ArtsEdNet

http://www.artsednet.getty.edu/

ArtsEdNet is an online arts education service for grades K-12 sponsored by the Getty Center for Education in the Arts. The site includes online exhibits, the latest trends in art education, lesson plans, and other curriculum resources.

ArtsEdNet Lesson Plans

http://www.artsednet.getty.edu/ArtsEdNet/Resources/index.html

ArtsEdNet Lesson Plans is an online service for K-12 arts education from the Getty Center for Education in the Arts. Teachers can find innovative lesson plans for the elementary school, middle school, and high school levels.

Crayola Art Education Lesson Plans

http://education.crayola.com/lessons/

Crayola Art Education Lesson Plans provide K-12 teachers with a variety of lesson plans that help guide students to recognize that creative communication involves not only language and visual arts, but social studies, science and math. Users can search by products (crayons, markers, colored pencils, etc.), subject area and age.

Explore Art

http://members.aol.com/powers8696/artindex.html

Explore Art is authored by Connie M. Powers and provides lesson plans, activities, and links to additional sites for art fun and games.

Eyes on Art

http://www.kn.pacbell.com/wired/art2/index.html

Eyes on Art, sponsored by Pacific Bell, provides seven visual art/Web-based lesson plans and a teacher's guide for K-12 classes.

Favorite Lessons

http://www.artswire.org/kenroar/lessons/
lessons.html

Favorite Lessons features plans and activities for grades K-12. Click a category to find a step-by-step explanation for a variety of topics, including Matisse Face Masterpiece, Table Murals, Monster Transformation, Masks and More Masks, and Too Loose Posters. The site also includes a form for submitting your favorite lesson.

Instructional Materials in Art

http://www.cln.org/subjects/art_inst.html

Instructional Materials in Art presented by Community Learning Network focuses on specific topics within Art. The site provides links to instructional materials (lesson plans) as well as general art resources.

KinderArt

http://www.kinderart.com/lessons.htm

KinderArt, provided by the Jarea Art Studio, features more than 100 free art lesson plans of every kind for kids ages 4-12. Topics include drawing, painting, printmaking, sculpture, multicultural art, cross-curricular art lessons, and coloring pages. The site also offers seasonal activities and art recipes in the Kinder Art Littles section.

Modern Art Lesson Plans

http://www.utah.edu/umfa/modern.html

Modern Art Lesson Plans, for grades 7-12, contains a collection of lesson plans from the Utah Museum of Fine Arts on the work of modern artists such as Robert Indiana, Victor Vasarely, and Andy Warhol.

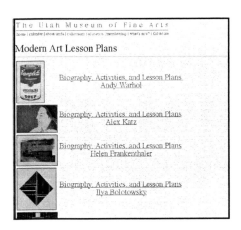

Visual Arts 8 to 10

http://www.bced.gov.bc.ca/irp/visart810/vatoc.htm

Visual Arts 8 to 10, provided by British Columbia's Ministry of Education, contains an integrated resource package of lesson plans for the visual arts in grades 8, 9, and 10.

Visual Arts 11 and 12

http://www.bced.gov.bc.ca/irp/va1112/vatoc.htm

Visual Arts 11 and 12 provided by British Columbia's Ministry of Education, contains an integrated resource package of lesson plans for the visual arts in grades 11 and 12.

About.com: Art for Kids

http://kidsartscrafts.about.com/arts/kidsartscrafts/mbody.htm

About.com: Art for Kids provides a wide variety of art education sites for grades K-12. The site includes online coloring books and printable coloring pages, as well as many activities and games.

A. Pintura: Art Detective

http://www.eduweb.com/pintura/

A. Pintura: Art Detective, produced by Educational Web Adventures, is an online game about art history and art composition suitable for grades 4 and up. Students learn how to look at art by becoming "Art Detectives" and traveling to some of the world's major museums. As the detectives search for famous artworks, they complete exercises and learn about the artists and their art. A worksheet for assessment and accountability and a teacher key for guidance in correcting are available.

Art Kids Rule!

http://artkidsrule.com/

Art Kids Rule! is a place for playing, learning, and creating. Kids can paint a picture, take a photo, and answer art quizzes. Teachers can search for lesson plans and activities and find links to other relevant resources.

Art Safari

http://artsafari.moma.org/

Art Safari allows kids to explore paintings and sculptures from the Museum of Modern Art accompanied by a series of questions where they are encouraged to write about what they observe. They can also submit their own art work.

Art Teacher on the Net

http://www.artmuseums.com/

Art Teacher on the Net provides a list of annotated links to numerous art projects for grades 4-12.

Coloring.com

http://coloring.com/

Coloring.com is an interactive coloring book for primary school pupils. Kids can color pictures online from a variety of categories and e-mail their pictures to family and friends.

Craft Finder

http://family.go.com/crafts

Craft Finder, by *Family Fun Magazine*, is an interactive Web site offering elementary school kids the chance to select materials from a list which Craft Finder then puts together and suggests ideas for great projects.

CyberSketchbook and Digital Drawing Board

http://www.vvm.com/~tgibbons/sketchbook/drawingboard.htm

CyberSketchbook and Digital Drawing Board emphasizes computer generated graphics and animation (K-12) and also focuses on the traditional study of drawing, painting, and sculpture. In addition, there is a collection of about a dozen lesson plans which include advice on Internet extensions and interdisciplinary application.

DLTK's Printable Crafts for Kids

http://dltk-kids.com/

DLTK's Crafts for Kids features a variety of fun children's crafts and coloring pages, including projects for holidays, educational themes, and children's favorite cartoon characters. There are lots of crafts to make for space study and science and printable templates suitable for preschoolers and elementary school children. For each craft, you'll find a detailed materials list, mostly everyday household items, and instructions.

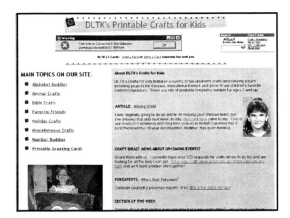

Educational Standards and Curriculum Frameworks for Art and Music

http://PutnamValleySchools.org/StSu/Art.html

Educational Standards and Curriculum Frameworks for Art and Music is an annotated list of Internet sites with K-12 educational standards and curriculum frameworks documents, maintained by Charles Hill and the Putnam Valley Schools in New York.

Emmett Scott's Arts & Activities

http://www.cartooncorner.com/artspage.html

Emmett Scott's Arts & Activities, for grades K-5, provides step-by-step instructions for drawing cartoons, as well as special tricks for creating them.

The Imagination Factory

http://users.hsonline.net/kidatart/

The Imagination Factory teaches children and teachers creative ways to recycle by making art with the trash they usually discard. The site contains lessons and activities as well as other relevant resources.

Joseph Wu's Origami Page

http://www.origami.vancouver.bc.ca/

Joseph Wu's Origami Page is the ultimate origami site, with extensive resources and information for K-12 teachers.

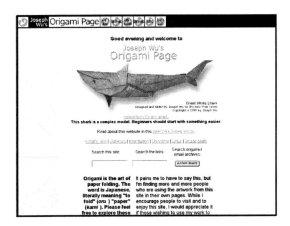

Kennedy Center's ArtsEdge

http://artsedge.kennedy-center.org/

Kennedy Center's ArtsEdge provides a forum where teachers and students can share information and ideas that support the arts in the K–12 curriculum.

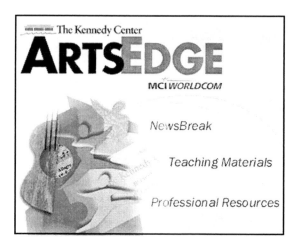

Stage Hand Puppets: The Activity Page

http://www3.ns.sympatico.ca/onstage/puppets/

Stage Hand Puppets: The Activity Page, for elementary classes, contains tips and patterns for making paper and scrap hand puppets. The site also includes short puppet plays written by kids.

Web Gallery of Art

http://gallery.euroweb.hu/index1.html

The Web Gallery of Art, maintained by Emil Kren and Daniel Marx of the Hungarian Academy of Sciences, contains a collection of more than 7,300 digital reproductions of European paintings and sculptures created between the years 1150 and 1750. Many of the pictures include commentaries and biographical information. If you can't find a painting or artwork in this collection, then scroll to acknowledgements, click on public sites on the Internet, and visit Mark Harden's site and others.

World Art Treasures WWW Server

http://sgwww.epfl.ch/BERGER/index.html

World Art Treasures WWW Server, sponsored by the Jacques-Edouard Berger Foundation, presents a series of online art programs. These include art from Egypt, China, Japan, India, Myanmar/Burma, Laos, Cambodia, and Thailand. Other programs include the works of Sandro Botticelli and Johannes Vermeer.

Yahoo! Arts: Art History: Masters

http://www.yahoo.com/Arts/Artists/Masters/

Yahoo! Arts: Art History: Masters is a Yahoo! Index with links to information on the lives and works of famous artists from around the world.

Asian Arts

www.webart.com/asianart/

Asian Arts is an electronic journal for the study and exhibition of arts of Asia. For an online tour, click Exhibitions and Galleries. The site includes articles and links to other relevant resources.

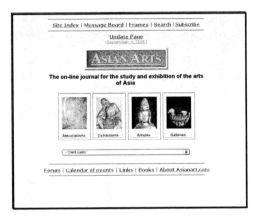

Diego Rivera

http://www.diegorivera.com/diego_home_eng.html

Diego Rivera is an exhibit that provides an in-depth study of the life and work of one of Mexico's most famous artists. A Spanish version is available.

Francisco Goya

http://goya.unizar.es

Francisco Goya presents the life of the famous Spanish artist accompanied by illustrations of his important works. A Spanish version is available.

The Global Show-n-Tell Museum

http://www.telenaut.com/gst/

The Global Show-n-Tell Museum provides a place where children of all ages can exhibit their art. There are detailed instructions on how kids can submit their work.

Museo del Prado

http://www.mcu.es/prado/index_eng.html

Museo del Prado offers information about the museum itself, a quick tour of 49 of its best-known works of art, a temporary exhibit celebrating the 250th anniversary of Goya, and links to other museums on the Web. A Spanish-language version is available.

The Virtual Museum for Children

http://www.museums.reading.ac.uk/children/#museums

The Virtual Museums for Children presents links to children's museums throughout the world.

Treasures of The Louvre

http://www.paris.org/Musees/Louvre/Treasures/

Treasures of The Louvre presents Paintings, Egyptian Antiquities, Oriental Antiquities, Greek, Etruscan and Roman Antiquities, Sculpture, Prints and Drawings, and Objets d'Art.

World Wide Web Virtual Library Museums Page

http://www.comlab.ox.ac.uk/archive/other/museums.html

World Wide Web Virtual Library Museums Page contains museums by country and continent, as well as selected virtual museums.

Biligual Education

Paso Partners: Integrating Mathematics, Science and Language

http://www.sedl.org/scimath/pasopartners/

Paso Partners offers a K-3 bilingual (Spanish/English) curriculum guide containing integrated lesson plans based on science themes. The guide includes suggested teacher/student materials and assessment procedures.

Washington State University Thematic Units

http://www.educ.wsu.edu/esl/Thematic_Units.html

Washington State University education students provide thematic units for a variety of topics that can be used in K-12 bilingual classrooms.

Amigos

http://edweb.sdsu.edu/people/cguanipa/amigos/

Amigos is an interactive online site for ethnically diverse middle school and high school students, parents, teachers and interested adults. They can share stories, swap experiences, find information or ask questions. Spanish and English versions are available.

Art Capades for K-3 Bilingual

http://www.kn.pacbell.com/wired/capades/

Art Capades for K-3 Bilingual, sponsored by Pacific Bell, features online activities for young bilingual children accompanied by tips for using the activities in the classroom.

Bilingual Books for Kids

http://www.bilingualbooks.com/

Bilingual Books for Kids provides a top-10 list and ordering information for books written with Spanish and English appearing side-by-side. The books introduce bilingual skills, increase language and learning abilities, and heighten awareness of many cultures.

Center for the Study of Books in Spanish for Children and Adolescents

http://www.csusm.edu/csbs/

Center for the Study of Books in Spanish for Children and Adolescents is sponsored by California State University at San Marcos. The center endeavors to maintain strong ties with organizations interested in meeting the needs of young readers. The center provides a schedule of workshops, names and addresses of publishers, bibliographies, and listings of recommended books. A Spanish version of the Web site is available.

Cinco de Mayo

http://latino.sscnet.ucla.edu/demo/cinco.html

Cinco de Mayo is a pictorial tour of the famous battle that celebrates the victory of Mexican forces over the French in the 19th century.

Electronic Textbook: Bilingual Education

http://www.ecsu.ctstateu.edu/depts/edu/textbooks/bilingual.html

Electronic Textbook: Bilingual Education provides links to various information on the Internet concerning bilingual education.

Enlaces bilingües para niños y maestros

http://members.tripod.com/~hamminkj/bilingue.html

These are Internet sites, mostly in Spanish, for elementary school pupils. They include games, poems and stories. In addition, there are links to lesson plans for teachers and information for parents.

Especially Español

http://www.kn.pacbell.com/wired/espanol/

Especially Español features Spanish language resources suitable for bilingual classes. Included are activities and resources appropriate for elementary students, middle and high school students, as well as links to professional bilingual educator sites, Internet tutorials, and other resources.

Estrellita Accelerated Beginning Spanish Reading

http://www.estrellita.com/index.html

Estrellita Accelerated Beginning Spanish Reading provides a description of an educational reading program in Spanish for Spanish speakers. The program can be used by teachers in elementary school bilingual classrooms. Scroll down the page and click these links for additional information and materials for teaching in bilingual classrooms: Bilingual Education Resources on the Net, Primary Education (K-3) Resources For Bilingual Educators, and Latino Resources on the Net.

Hot Internet Sites en Español

http://www.kn.pacbell.com/wired/spanish

Hot Internet Sites en Español is an internet hotlist of Spanish resources created by Beth Bustamante and Pacific Bell Education First and appropriate for grades K-community college. Teachers will find resources for students who are native speakers as well as for students learning Spanish as a foreign language. Included are lesson plans and activities for use with or without a computer.

Juegos y Canciones para Niños

http://www.hevanet.com/dshivers/juegos/

Spanish games and songs for children. Most of the songs included come from a CD called Naranja Dulce: Juegos Infantiles Compañia Infantil de Televicentro de Armando Torres. The CD is published by BMG in Mexico.

Kokone

http://www.kokone.com.mx/

This interactive online Spanish-language children's site is about Mexico's culture. El Tlacuache, an opossum-like creature, is the animated guide. Students will find games and riddles, a Latin American cooking section, an animals and eco-adventure section, a life through the eyes of the children of Mexico section, a literature section, and a historical section.

Lugares en Español para Niños

http://www.ala.org/parentspage/greatsites/
arts2.html#g

Los sitios se recomiendan para los niños de edad pre-escolar hasta, e incluyendo, los catorce años, sus padres y aquellos quienes los cuidan.

Mexico for Kids

http://explora.presidencia.gob.mx/index_kids.html

Mexico for Kids, written in French and Spanish as well as English for elementary school students, features a guide, El Balero, who takes youngsters on a tour of the geography, history, and government of Mexico.

Mundo Latino Educación el Rinconcito

http://www.mundolatino.org/rinconcito/

Mundo Latino Educación el Rinconcito is an interactive site which features activities, games, and stories for Spanish-speaking elementary school pupils. Mundo Latino Rinconcito also includes a bulletin board for children and links to more children's sites.

National Clearinghouse for Bilingual Education

http://www.ncbe.gwu.edu/

National Clearinghouse for Bilingual Education (NCBE) is funded by the U.S. Department of Education's Office of Bilingual Education and Minority Languages Affairs (OBEMLA). NCBE collects, analyzes, and disseminates information related to the effective education of linguistically and culturally diverse K–12 learners in the United States. The site includes an online library, language and education links, databases, and links to publishers and distributors of teaching materials. You can also subscribe to an e-mail news bulletin and an electronic discussion group.

Paso Partners

http://www.sedl.org/scimath/pasopartners/
pphome.html

Paso Partners provides bilingual (English/Spanish) lesson plans for K–3 students which integrate science, math and language. Plans include Five Senses (Los Cinco Sentidos), Spiders, (Las Arañas), and Dinosaurs (Los Dinosauros).

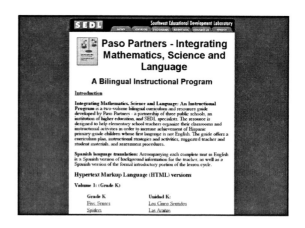

Drama

Classroom Lesson Plans

http://www.geocities.com/Broadway/Alley/3765/lessons.html

Classroom Lesson Plans, produced by Matt Buchanan, contains more than 35 lesson plans for creative drama classes. Most of these lesson plans work with a large age range (with appropriate adjustments in level of sophistication) and are organized by age level, type, and cross curricular content.

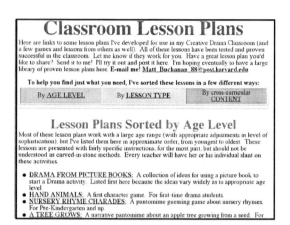

Drama 8 to 10

http://www.bced.gov.bc.ca/irp/drama810/drtoc.htm

Drama 8 to 10, from the British Columbia Ministry of Education, features an integrated resource package of lesson plans for teaching dance and drama in grades 8, 9, and 10.

Drama Storytelling, Creative Dramatics, Puppetry & Readers Theater for Children & Young Adults

http://falcon.jmu.edu/~ramseyil/drama.htm

Drama Storytelling, Creative Dramatics, Puppetry & Readers Theater for Children & Young Adults provides teachers with resources for oral interpretation of literature through dramatic activity, storytelling, and reader's theater. Among the links available are Reader's Theater Scripts and Lesson Plans K–8, which feature lessons on creative dramatics, creative thinking, creativity, elements in drama, exposition, script starters, and expressive speech.

The Drama Teacher's Resource Room

http://www3.sk.sympatico.ca/erachi/

The Drama Teacher's Resource Room features creative and challenging experiences for students in the drama classroom. It offers lesson plans, articles on costume, props, set design, lighting and scenic painting, and links to other resources.

Drama Workshop: Ideas for Teaching Drama

http://members.tripod.co.uk/Andrew_Felton_McCann/index-4.html

Drama Workshop: Ideas for Teaching Drama, prepared by Andrew McCann, is a collection of ideas for teaching drama in theatre workshop contexts and youth theatre groups as well as for developing spoken language skills in classrooms across a variety of age and ability ranges. The ideas use role play and dramatic improvisation and are classified according to theme.

ProTeacher: Drama

http://www.proteacher.com/080010.shtml

ProTeacher: Drama provides links to lesson plans, activities, and resources for K-12 teachers of theatre.

Theatre for Young Audiences: Creative Drama

http://www.geocities.com/Broadway/Alley/3765/

Theatre for Young Audiences: Creative Drama, developed by Matt Buchanan, provides plays to produce, lesson plans for the drama classroom, a bibliography of helpful books, definitions of terms with discussion, monologues for young performers, a list of great links, and additional resources.

Theatre Lesson Plan Exchange

http://www.geocities.com/Shalyndria13

Theatre Lesson Plan Exchange includes lesson plans, warm-ups, games, improvs, assessment, and additional links to theatre resources.

DRAMA   **OTHER RESOURCES**

British Theatre

http://britishtheatre.miningco.com/

British Theatre is the Mining Company's guide to the whole spectrum of British theater, from musicals to Shakespeare. The site looks at the performers and the writers, the stars and the wannabes. The site is suitable for high school English and drama classes.

Children's Creative Theatre

http://tqjunior.advanced.org/5291/

Children's Creative Theatre was produced by children for children. It features a short history of theater, a glossary of theater terms, creative dramatics games and activities, a skit, quizzes, and more. The teacher's resource section contains cross-curriculum based ideas and is organized by grade level and subject area.

Children's Theatre

http://faculty-web.at.nwu.edu/theater/tya/

Children's Theatre provides links to resources and information of interest to teachers involved in theatre for young audiences.

Dramatists Play Service

http://www.dramatists.com/text/main.html

Dramatists Play Service has worked with both nonprofessional and professional theater groups to provide plays available for production. Teachers will find a listing of plays by title, author, and number of characters, as well as information on obtaining nonprofessional performance rights.

The Educational Theatre Association

http://www.etassoc.org/eta-home.htm

The Educational Theatre Association (ETA) is devoted to promoting and supporting educational theater programs, primarily at the middle school and high school levels. ETA publishes a monthly magazine, *Dramatics*, and a quarterly publication, *Teaching Theatre*. For a list of useful and interesting theater-oriented sites on the World Wide Web, click on The Resource Pool and then on Education Links.

High School Theatre

http://www.fn.net/~east22/HSprograms.html

High School Theatre is maintained by the Theatre Arts Department at Wichita High School East. The site provides links to Acting; Broadway and Ticket Information; General Theatre; Magazines and Journals; Playwrights, Lyricists, and Composers; Publishers; and Technical Theatre. It also allows teachers and students to search a collection of other high school theater sites on the Web.

Playbill Online

http://www1.playbill.com/playbill/

Playbill Online provides theater listings, newsletters, a multimedia center, job opportunities, links to theater resources, and much more. This resource should interest anyone considering drama as a career.

Samuel French

http://www.samuelfrench.com/

Samuel French is the world's oldest play publisher and caters to film and theater professionals and students. It provides the largest selection of plays in the world. Teachers can browse an alphabetical list of book titles.

School Show Page

http://www.schoolshows.demon.co.uk/

School Show Page contains a variety of online resources for school and youth theater in Grades K–12. You'll find articles on playwriting in the archive section, a list of plays and guides for the classroom in the download section, and new plays in the What's New section. You can also contact U.S. schools about their theater arts programs.

Scott's Theatre Links

http://www.theatre-link.com/

Scott's Theatre Links provides links to information about Broadway and Off-Broadway shows and their lyrics and music, as well as links to Shakespeare's works and Shakespeare festivals.

Theatre Central

http://www1.playbill.com/cgi-bin/plb/central?cmd=start

Theatre Central provides a large directory of theater resources on the Web.

Yahoo! Arts: Drama: Musicals

http://www.yahoo.com/Arts/Performing_Arts/Theater/Musicals/

Yahoo! Arts: Drama: Musicals provides relevant information for high school drama students and teachers. It includes links to Movies, Shows, Songwriters, and Theater Groups.

English as a Second Language

Adult Education ESL Teachers Guide

http://humanities.byu.edu/elc/Teacher/
TeacherGuideMain

Adult Education ESL Teachers Guide is written and produced by C. Ray Graham and Mark M. Walsh. The lesson plans can be adapted for secondary school students. Links include Beginning ESL Lessons and Accompanying Teacher Training Modules, Intermediate ESL Lessons and Accompanying Teacher Training Modules, and Teaching Non-Literate Adults. All materials and worksheets are provided.

English Club Teacher's Room

http://www.englishclub.net/teachers/index.htm

English Club Teacher's Room includes lesson plans, activities and handouts for teaching EFL and ESL.

ESL Lessons

http://members.aol.com/Jakajk/ESLLessons.html

ESL Lessons provides many lessons and activities for enriching ESL classes. The site also includes links to other relevant ESL materials.

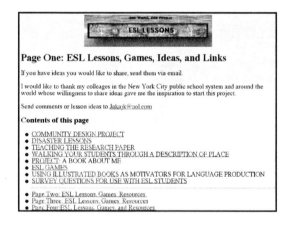

Internet TESL Journal for Teachers of ESL

http://www.aitech.ac.jp/~iteslj/

The **Internet TESL Journal for Teachers of ESL** is a monthly Web magazine featuring lesson plans and lesson ideas.

Karin's ESL Party Land

http://www.eslpartyland.com/

ESL Party Land provides teachers with lesson plans and printable materials to use in class and provides students with more than 50 interactive quizzes, 15 discussion forums, and additional links.

PIZZAZ! A Resource for Scribblers and Teachers of English as a Second Language

http://darkwing.uoregon.edu/~leslieob/pizzaz.html

PIZZAZ! A Resource for Scribblers and Teachers of English as a Second Language, produced by Leslie Opp-Beckman, is dedicated to providing creative writing activities and reproducible handouts for use in ESL classrooms for grades 7-12.

TESL: Lessons

http://www.aitech.ac.jp/~iteslj/links/TESL/Lessons/

TESL: Lessons is sponsored by the *Internet TESL Journal* and features links to a large variety of lesson plans and activities relevant for teachers of grades 7-12.

Dave's ESL Cafe on the Web

http://www.pacificnet.net/~sperling/eslcafe.html

Dave's ESL Cafe on the Web is open 24 hours a day for ESL students and teachers from around the world. Scroll down the page and select from a variety of cafe items. You can take an interactive quiz in the ESL Quiz Center, receive help with questions related to English in the ESL Help Center, search for something in the cafe or on the Web at the One-Stop ESL Search Page, share your experiences with others on the ESL Idea Page, read and add your own writings to the ESL Graffiti Wall, or ask a question of Dave on the ESL Question Page. There are also links to other ESL information for both students and teachers, an interactive message exchange, an ESL e-mail connection and a job center. The site is suitable for grades 9-12.

English Grammar Links for ESL Students

http://www.gl.umbc.edu/~kpokoy1/grammar1.htm

English Grammar Links for ESL Students, created by Karen M. Hartman, provides links to grammar references, exercises, and quizzes that can help ESL teachers and students in grades 7-12.

EnglishPractice.com

http://englishpractice.com/

EnglishPractice.com provides online lessons for improving grammar, vocabulary, and reading skills. Also includes chat rooms and an e-mail newsletter.

English Page

http://englishpage.com/

English Page offers free exercises and resources for intermediate and advanced English learners.

Ernie's EFL Page

http://barteldes.freeyellow.com/index.html

Ernie's EFL Page includes among its topics: EFL Activities and Games, EFL Song Activities, EFL Writing Page Links, Book Review of The Month, CD Review of The Month, EFL texts, and a video activities page.

ESL Standards for PreK-12 Students

http://www.tesol.edu/assoc/k12standards/it/01.html

ESL Standards for PreK-12 Students is clustered by grade level (PreK-3, 4-8, and 9-12) and addresses varying degrees of proficiency (beginner, intermediate, advanced), as well as the needs of ESL students with limited formal schooling. The standards use vignettes of actual instructional sequences in which teachers help students meet the standards in diverse settings (such as social studies or math).

everythingESL.Net

http://www.everythingESL.net/

everythingESL.Net features resources for ESL teachers working with K-12 language minority students. The site includes lesson plans, information, staff inservicing, activities, bulletin boards and more.

Interesting Things for ESL Students

http://www.aitech.ac.jp/~itesls/

Interesting Things for ESL Students is a fun study site for students of English as a Second Language. It contains word games, puzzles, quizzes, slang, proverbs and much more.

Learning English on the Web

http://www.rong-chang.com/

Learning English on the Web is a starting point for ESL learners in grades 7–12 who want to learn English on the World Wide Web. The site includes listening, speaking, reading, and writing activities.

TESL: Lessons

http://www.aitech.ac.jp/~iteslj/links/TESL/Lessons/

TESL: Lessons is sponsored by the Internet TESL Journal and features links to a large variety of lesson plans and activities relevant for teachers of grades 7-12.

TESL/TEFL/TESOL/ESL/EFL/ESOL Links

http://www.aitech.ac.jp/~iteslj/ESL3.html

TESL/TEFL/TESOL/ESL/EFL/ESOL Links is a mega index of resources for the ESL teacher. It provides links to a wide variety of sites from Associations and Computer Assisted Language Learning, to Games, Poetry, and Song Lyrics.

TESOL Online

http://www.tesol.edu

TESOL Online, from Teachers of English to Speakers of Other Languages, the international professional association of ESL teachers, includes links to publications available from TESOL, as well as selected articles from *TESOL Journal* and *TESOL Quarterly.*

Foreign Language

Activités

http://voila.heinle.com/title.htm

Activités, authored by Terri Nelson, Cal State University-San Bernardino, provides 20 lessons and activities suitable for intermediate students of French.

Blue Web'n Learning Applications

http://www.kn.pacbell.com/wired/bluewebn/

Blue Web'n Learning Applications, provided by Pacific Bell, includes lessons, activities, projects, resources, references, and tools. Scroll to Content Table, Foreign Language to find the materials.

Bonjour!

http://www.bonjour.org.uk/

Bonjour!, produced by The Howard School in Rainham, Kent, England, presents its content in French. The site includes grammar guides, as well as lists of vocabulary about different topics such as weather, and time. Students can use basic and advanced dialogues.

Cambridge School Classics Project

http://www.caecilius.com/

This site presents information for students who are learning Latin. The site has a translator, where students can type in English and retrieve their Latin sentences. There are many fun activities, including a Latin word search (with clues in English and solutions in Latin) and a caption contest.

Cooperative Learning in Modern Languages

http://www.geocities.com/Paris/LeftBank/3852/cooplearn.html

Cooperative Learning in Modern Languages was prepared by Pete Jones of the Pine Ridge Secondary School in Ontario (Canada). The site features lessons useful for creating a student-centered language class which teachers can print out. Several of the activities are available for languages other than French.

Especially Español

http://pomo.kn.pacbell.com/wired/espanol/index.html

Especially Español contains lesson plans and online activities for elementary, middle and high school levels. Additional resources are also included.

Hot Internet Sites en Español

http://www.kn.pacbell.com/wired/spanish

Hot Internet Sites en Español is an Internet hotlist of Spanish resources created by Beth Bustamante and Pacific Bell Education First and appropriate for grades K-community college. Teachers will find resources for students who are native speakers as well as for students learning Spanish as a foreign language. Included are lesson plans and activities for use with or without a computer.

Internet Activities for Foreign Language Classes

http://members.aol.com/maestro12/web/wadir.html

Internet Activities for Foreign Language Classes contains online lesson plans and student worksheets for using foreign language Web sites in high school German, French, Japanese and Spanish classes. Each worksheet presents students with questions, activities, and corresponding Web sites students must access to complete the assignment. Worksheets can be printed out and used by the whole class or by individuals for homework.

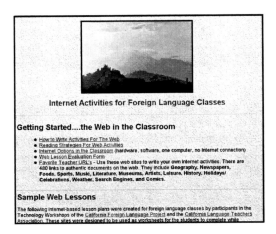

Lesson Ideas Para La Clase

http://www.teachspanish.com/

Lesson Ideas Para La Clase, from TeachSpanish.Com, includes lesson Ideas (K-12), Spanish-speaking country information, a Teacher Job Search, hundreds of links to teacher resources, teacher Web sites, student hot spots, Latin/Spanish music sites, schools and study abroad, and a teacher and student discussion board.

Teacher Resource Sites

http://www.teachspanish.com/links/resources.html

Teacher Resource Sites provided by TeachSpanish.com, feature lesson ideas and activities for the classroom.

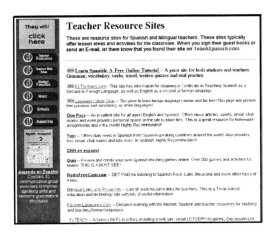

World Language Lesson Plans

http://members.aol.com/Donnpages/2LessonPlans.html#FOREIGN

World Language Lesson Plans includes lesson plans and activities for English as a Second Language instruction, Foreign Language instruction, Spanish, German, French, Latin, and more.

Advanced Placement Program

http://www.collegeboard.org/ap/subjects.html

Advanced Placement Program, provided by the College Board Online, features tips for teachers and students, information about AP classes and exams, and related Web sites for all AP subjects, including French, German, and Spanish.

AltaVista Translation Service

http://babelfish.altavista.com/translate.dyn

AltaVista Translation Service allows users to enter text or a URL and have it translated into another language.

American Association of Teachers of French

http://aatf.utsa.edu/

American Association of Teachers of French (AATF) promotes the study of French through its 75 chapters and its official publications. The site includes links to other resources of interest to teachers of French.

American Classical League

http://www.umich.edu/~acleague/

American Classical League (ACL) includes teachers of Latin, Greek, and Classics on elementary, secondary, and college levels. The ACL Web site contains information on teaching materials, scholarships, and teacher placement.

American Council on the Teaching of Foreign Languages

http://www.actfl.org/

American Council on the Teaching of Foreign Languages (ACTFL) is the professional association that represents teachers of all languages at all educational levels. The ACTFL site contains information on a variety of topics, including professional development programs, proficiency testing publications, and job opportunities.

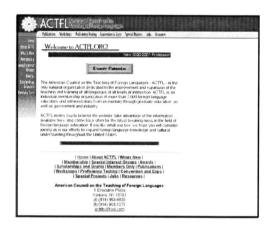

An Online In-service Course For Training Foreign Language Teachers In Internet Technologies

http://www.ea.pvt.k12.pa.us/htm/Units/Upper/modlang/inserv.htm

An Online In-service Course for Training Foreign Language Teachers In Internet Technologies is designed to help Foreign Language classroom teachers adapt and use communications technology in their K-12 classrooms and to design and share ideas with others.

Civilization francaise

http://www.cortland.edu/flteach/civ/

Civilization française, developed by Marie Ponterio, consists of online teaching modules, which include original images, audiocues, and digital videos. The modules are based on a wide range of topics such as cuisine, culture, social change, school, economy, Europe, holidays, family life, housing, history, religion, social security, symbols, transportation and vacation.

ClicNet

http://www.swarthmore.edu/Humanities/clicnet/

ClicNet édite ou localise des ressources virtuelles en français pour les étudiants, les enseignants de français langue étrangère (FLE) ou langue seconde (FLS), et tous ceux qui s'intéressent aux cultures, aux arts et aux littératures francophones. No English version is available.

Clip Art Collection for Foreign/ Second Language Instruction

http://www.sla.purdue.edu/fll/JapanProj/FLClipart/

Clip Art Collection for Foreign/Second Language Instruction provides a series of hand-drawn pictures illustrating verbs, adjectives, and common nouns that teachers can print out and use in the classroom.

Communication Connections

http://www.widomaker.com/~ldprice/#Pelusa

Communication Connections, designed by Lora Price, a teacher at Gloucester High School in Virginia, is a menu of Web sites dedicated to the study, use, and enjoyment of languages. Although many cultures and languages are represented, specialized listings have been provided for French, German, Latin, Italian, Japanese, and Spanish. At this site, you can consult original sources, use a foreign language dictionary, take a language course, navigate metro systems, and read the daily news or listen to music from the country of your choice.

Educational Standards and Curriculum Frameworks for Foreign Language/ESL

http://PutnamValleySchools.org/StSu/FLang.html

Educational Standards and Curriculum Frameworks for Foreign Language/ESL is an annotated list of Internet sites with K-12 educational standards and curriculum frameworks documents, maintained by Charles Hill and the Putnam Valley Schools in New York.

Fast and Friendly French for Fun

http://library.thinkquest.org/12447/

Fast and Friendly French for Fun is an online interactive site geared for the middle school level. There's a guided tour of the site; a Geography, People, and Food tour of France; a set of introductory lessons, including All-Purpose Phrases; and a game.

Foreign Language Multimedia Evaluation Project

http://nts.lll.hawaii.edu/flmedia/default.htm

The **Foreign Language Multimedia Evaluation Project** at the University of Hawaii National Foreign Language Resource Center offers an extensive listing of multimedia software, CDs, and Web resources along with online evaluations.

Foreign Language News and Magazine Page

http://libraries.mit.edu/humanities/flnews/

Foreign Language News and Magazine Page features online newspapers and magazines in a variety of languages, including Chinese, French, German, Italian, Japanese, Portuguese, Russian and Spanish.

Foreign Language Study Abroad for Teachers

http://www.csun.edu/~hcedu013/LanguageAbroad.html

Foreign Language Study Abroad for Teachers features links to hundreds of foreign language schools in dozens of countries where teachers can upgrade their language skills. Also included is a directory of High School Foreign Exchange and Language Study Programs suitable for teenagers.

Foreign Language Teaching Forum

http://www.cortland.edu/www/flteach/welcome.htmlx

Foreign Language Teaching Forum (FL Teach) provides resources for classroom activities, curriculum, and syllabus design. It features Web links to foreign language resources organized by language. Information is provided on subscribing to a mailing list that allows you to ask a question about a topic, share an idea or lesson plan, or just read what your fellow teachers say. Messages will appear in your e-mail. You can also search the FL Teach archives and read previous messages.

German Studies Trails on the Web

http://www2.uncg.edu/~lixlpurc/german.html

German Studies Trails on the Web, compiled by Andreas Lixl-Purcell, professor of German at the University of North Carolina at Greensboro, lists some of the most useful interdisciplinary German resources on the World Wide Web. You can select from a variety of topics, such as German Language and Culture (Sprache und Landeskunde), Arts and Humanities (Kunst und Wissenschaft), and Education and Research (Unterricht und Forschung).

High School Foreign Exchange and Language Study Programs

http://www.csun.edu/~hcedu013/karin.html

High School Foreign Exchange and Language Study Programs was designed by Karin Levine, a Spanish teacher at Thousand Oaks (California) High School. The site features links to organizations sponsoring high school foreign exchange programs and language study programs abroad for teens.

Intercultural E-Mail Classroom Connections

http://www.stolaf.edu/network/iecc/

The IECC (Intercultural E-Mail Classroom Connections) mailing lists are provided by St. Olaf College as a free service to help teachers and classes link with partners in other countries and cultures for e-mail classroom pen-pal and project exchanges.

The Latin Page (Salvete Ad Paginam Latinam)

http://www.geocities.com/Athens/Acropolis/3773/

The Latin Page (Salvete Ad Paginam Latinam) provides general classroom resources designed primarily for the Latin teacher in grades 7–12. Some projects may be adapted for the lower grades.

Latinteach Classroom Ideas and Projects

http://www.latinteach.com/

Latinteach Classroom Ideas and Projects features some of the best ideas and projects from the Latinteach Mailing List for teachers of Latin at all levels.

'Más arriba' Home Page

http://www.trentu.ca/spanish/masarriba/

'Más arriba' Home Page, created by Gary D. Aitken, is an electronic workbook designed to accompany the second edition of ¡Arriba! Comunicación y cultura (Prentice Hall). The exercise material of Más arriba can be adapted for use with other core textbooks.

Resources for Students and Teachers of French as a Second Language

http://www.uottawa.ca/~weinberg/french.html

Resources for Students and Teachers of French as a Second Language is provided by the University of Ottawa, Canada. It features exercises and resources for students; resources for teachers; French in Canada, outside Quebec, in Quebec, and in France; Francophonie in the world; news and discussion groups; and miscellaneous links.

Taller hispano

http://www.cortland.edu/www/flteach/usafa/taller.html

Taller hispano, by Jean LeLoup, contains activity modules using authentic materials and Internet resources designed around themes such as the individual, the family, leisure activities and schools.

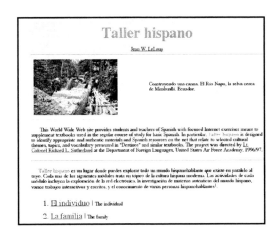

Tecla

http://www.bbk.ac.uk/tecla/

Tecla, an electronic magazine for learners and teachers of Spanish, is written by members of the Spanish Department at Birkbeck College, University of London. It appears weekly on the Web during the school year and consists of short readings followed by comprehension exercises.

Tennessee Bob's Famous French Links

http://www.utm.edu/departments/french/french.html

Tennessee Bob's Famous French Links provides useful resources for teachers and learners of French. Topics include Art and Special Image Exhibits; Literature and Music; Newspapers, Magazines, and Newsgroups; and Audiovisual (radio/TV).

Health and Physical Education

California Physical Education Instruction

http://www.stan-co.k12.ca.us/calpe/Instruction.html

California Physical Education Instruction provides teachers with model lessons. Scroll to the bottom of the page to find sample lesson plans for the elementary, middle and high school levels.

Game Central Station

http://gamecentralstation.com/

Game Central Station offers a list of more than 350 P.E. games in searchable database for grades PreK-12. For hundreds of other P.E. lesson plans, click on Links in the menu panel.

Games Kids Play

http://www.gameskidsplay.net/

Games Kids Play provides more than 500 playground games for grades preK-5. Each game has a description and rules.

Health Lesson Ideas

http://pe.central.vt.edu/lessonideas/health/healthlp.html

Health Lesson Ideas, from P.E. Central (sponsored by Virginia Tech), provides lessons for elementary school, middle school, and high school students.

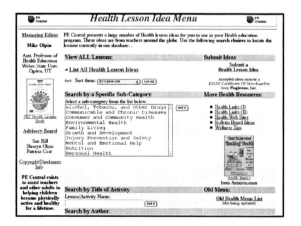

P.E. Central

http://pe.central.vt.edu/

P.E. Central is specifically designed for physical education teachers, students, interested parents, and adults. Sponsored by Virginia Tech, its goal is to provide the latest information about contemporary physical education programs for children. The site includes assessment ideas, lesson plans, activities of the week, P.E. people on the Web, links to other relevant sites, and information on how to subscribe to a mailing list.

P.E. Lesson Plans and Activities

http://www.sports-media.org/

P.E. Lesson Plans and Activities, from Sports Media, provides more than 50 lesson plans for all areas of the P.E. program.

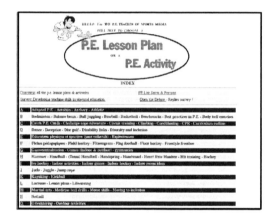

Physical Education K to 7

http://www.bced.gov.bc.ca/irp/pek7/petoc.htm

Physical Education K to 7, produced by the British Columbia Ministry of Education, contains P.E. lesson plans for students at the K-7 level.

Physical Education 8 to 10

http://www.bced.gov.bc.ca/irp/pe810/petoc.htm

Physical Education 8 to 10, sponsored by the British Columbia Ministry of Education, features P.E. lesson plans for students in grades 8-10.

Physical Education 11 to 12

http://www.bced.gov.bc.ca/irp/pe11_12/petoc.htm

Physical Education 11 to 12, from the British Columbia Ministry of Education, provides lesson plans for high school students.

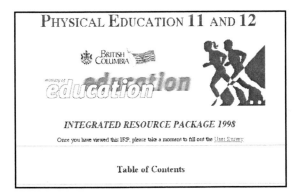

Physical Education Lesson Ideas

http://pe.central.vt.edu/lessonideas/
pelessonplans.html

Physical Education Lesson Ideas, from P.E. Central (sponsored by Virginia Tech), provides useful lessons for Pre-K, elementary school, middle school, and high school students.

Physical Education Lesson Plans

http://members.tripod.com/~pazz/lesson.html

This Web site offers a rich assortment of physical education lesson plans for the middle school submitted by P.E. teachers around the country. From "Bionic Ball" to "Batman and Robin," these fun and challenging activities will shake up students who were expecting a typical P.E. hour.

TeachersFirst's P.E. Lesson Plans

http://www.teachersfirst.com/lesn-pe.htm

TeachersFirst, sponsored by the Network for Instructional TV, provides hundreds of P.E. lessons for grades K-12, including adaptive physical education activites.

Adolescence Directory On-Line

http://education.indiana.edu/cas/adol/adol.html

Adolescence Directory On-Line (ADOL) is an electronic guide to information regarding adolescent issues and secondary education. It is maintained by the Center for Adolescent Studies, located in the School of Education, Indiana University, Bloomington. The site features electronic links to relevant health resources for teachers, kids, counselors, and parents. Link topics include Mental Health Issues, Health Issues, Conflict and Violence, Counselor Resources, and Teens Only.

Benny Goodsport

http://www.bennygoodsport.com/

Benny Goodsport provides information, activities, games, puzzles, and stories about sports and recreational activities for elementary school children.

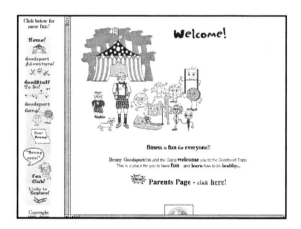

Dole 5 A Day Homepage

http://www.dole5aday.com/

Dole 5 A Day Homepage provides nutrition information about fruits and vegetables for elementary school students. It offers fun school activities for children, and teachers can order a free CD-ROM from Dole.

Dr. Pribut's Running Injuries Page

http://www.clark.net/pub/pribut/spsport.html

Dr. Pribut's Running Injuries Page offers runners, coaches, and teachers information on running injuries and how to prevent them. It also includes links to other sports pages.

Educational Standards and Curriculum Frameworks for Health

http://PutnamValleySchools.org/StSu/Health.html

Educational Standards and Curriculum Frameworks for Health is an annotated list of Internet sites with K-12 educational standards and curriculum frameworks documents, maintained by Charles Hill and the Putnam Valley Schools in New York.

Educational Standards and Curriculum Frameworks for Physical Education

http://PutnamValleySchools.org/StSu/PE.html

Educational Standards and Curriculum Frameworks for Physical Education is an annotated list of Internet sites with K-12 educational standards and curriculum frameworks documents, maintained by Charles Hill and the Putnam Valley Schools in New York.

Fronske Health Center's Health Education Page

http://www.nau.edu/~fronske/he.html

Fronske Health Center's Health Education Page provides information relevant to high school health teachers. Click Health Brochure for links to topics ranging from alcohol and AIDS to fitness and infectious diseases.

Go Ask Alice!

http://www.columbia.edu/cu/healthwise/

Go Ask Alice! is an interactive, health-related question-and-answer service on the Web. Health professionals at Columbia University provide the answers. Users can search archives for answers to previously asked questions.

International Food Information Council

http://ificinfo.health.org/

International Food Information Council (IFIC) offers a Web site that contains information about healthy and safe food choices for K-12 students. Click Information for Educators to find information about the new food label educational curriculum for grades 10-12, food insight reprints, and videotapes.

KidsHealth

http://kidshealth.org/index2.html

KidsHealth, a project sponsored by the Nemours Foundation Center for Biomedical Communication, is an interactive Web site providing health information. Click on Parents, Teens or Kids to find relevant resources. Students can play games, participate in polls and quizzes, and read a health tip of the day. They can even enter one of their own health tips and win a T-shirt.

KidSource OnLine Healthcare

http://www.kidsource.com/kidsource/pages/health.html

KidSource OnLine Healthcare provides health care information for K-12 teachers and parents.

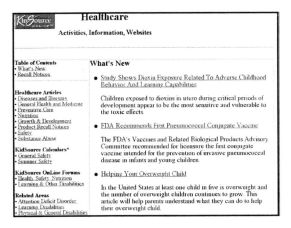

Multimedia Tutorials for Children and Parents

http://www.people.virginia.edu/~smb4v/tutorial.html

Multimedia Tutorials for Children and Parents, sponsored by Children's Medical Center of the University of Virginia, provides tutorials on asthma, cerebral palsy, and gastroesophageal reflux, with additional topics coming soon. Each tutorial features text, graphics, sound, and video.

Resources for School Health Educators

http://www.indiana.edu/~aphs/hlthk-12.html

Resources for School Health Educators, from the Department of Applied Health Science at Indiana University, provides teachers and high school students with a wide variety of relevant resources. Among its many links are those to information on school health education; national health organizations; alcohol, tobacco, and other drug education; violence prevention; first aid; sex education; and health education centers and museums.

SPARK Physical Education: "P.E. for the 21st Century"

http://www.foundation.sdsu.edu/projects/spark/index.html

SPARK Physical Education: "P.E. for the 21st Century" is an innovative K–6 physical education curriculum and staff development program. The SPARK program offers materials and services to schools and health organizations on a nonprofit basis through San Diego State University.

Sports Media

http://www.sports-media.org/

Sports Media is a nonprofit organization of physical education experts. The organization uses its Web site to present sports and physical education links and lesson plans. Original material and online advice is collected from coaches, educators, and other experts in all types of sports.

Worldguide Health & Fitness Forum

http://www.worldguide.com/hf.html

Worldguide Health & Fitness Forum provides high school physical education teachers, coaches, trainers, and athletes with links to a human anatomy lesson, exercise recommendations for power and speed, ideas on how to maintain a healthy heart, and nutritional information.

Yahoo! Recreation: Sports

http://www.yahoo.com/Recreation/Sports/

Yahoo! Recreation: Sports provides teachers, coaches, and children with links to relevant information for sports and games, from air hockey and wrestling to archery and water polo. The site also includes a link to Scoreboard, which provides up-to-the-minute scores and information. A search tool allows you to find more information about sports in the Yahoo! database.

Journalism

Schoolzone

http://www.nando.net/prof/edsvc/

Newspapers In Education's **SchoolZone** provides a variety of online newspaper lesson plans and activities for middle school and high school students. The site includes featured stories and a daily news quiz on current events, as well as other lesson ideas.

Teaching Media

http://www.media-awareness.ca/eng/med/class/teamedia.htm

Canada's Media Awareness Network offers a wide variety of K-12 lessons and units for teaching about the media. Topics consist of newspapers and magazines, television and radio, movies, and music.

For Journalism Teachers Only

http://jteacher.com

For Journalism Teachers Only contain a wealth of information and links for journalism teachers, publications advisers and student editors.

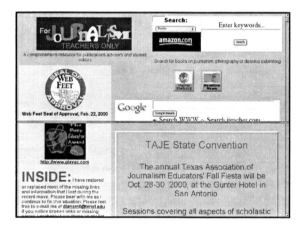

Highwired.Net

http://www.highwired.net/

Highwired.Net is the world's largest network of online high schools. Using their FREE and easy-to-use Web publishing tools, teachers and students can create Internet sites to build their own high school paper online.

Indiana University High School Journalism Institute

http://www.journalism.indiana.edu/workshops/HSJI/index.html

Indiana University High School Journalism Institute serves as a continuing education outreach program for secondary school students and their teachers. The Institute provides summer workshops and a number of newsletters and other publications supportive of secondary school journalism education.

Journalism Education Association

http://www.jea.org/

The **Journalism Education Association** is the only independent national scholastic journalism organization for teachers and advisers. Among JEA's 2,000 members are journalism teachers and publications advisers, media professionals, press associations, adviser organizations, libraries, yearbook companies, newspapers, radio stations and departments of journalism. The site includes a menu with links to information about conferences, curriculum helps, scholarships, books, and job opportunities.

Journalism Education Association of Northern California

http://www.jeanc.org/

Journalism Education Association of Northern California (jeanc) provides excellent resources for high school journalism students and their advisers, including a copy of California's Education Code explaining students' free speech rights and responsibilities and a Model Publications Code. Information about the Student Press Law Center, the Freedom Forum, and the national Journalism Education Association's position on student press rights is given. The site also includes a list of other journalism sites on the Web.

KidNews

http://www.kidnews.com/

KidNews is a news and writing service for elementary school and middle school students and teachers around the world. Using this free exchange service, teachers and children can gather news stories and ideas for their own school papers. KidNews includes news stories, feature stories, profiles, and sports stories, as well as information on other newspaper-related topics.

National Scholastic Press Association

http://studentpress.journ.umn.edu/

National Scholastic Press Association is a non-profit membership organization serving student journalists and advisers. Information is available about summer journalism workshops, journalism competitions, e-mail discussion lists, *The Best of High School Press Online*, and links to hundreds of useful resources.

Quill and Scroll

http://www.uiowa.edu/~quill-sc/index.html

Quill and Scroll is an international honorary society for high school journalists encouraging and recognizing individual student achievement in journalism and scholastic publication. The society sponsors an international writing, photo contest, a yearbook excellence contest, and a news media evaluation which is an in-depth critique of school newspapers.

The Write Site

http://www.writesite.org/

The Write Site is an interactive journalism project for middle schools. The site features a Newsroom for Students, and an Editor's Desk for Teachers. By taking the monthly Classroom Challenge, students can see how their class stacks up against other Write Site schools.

Yahoo! Individual School Papers

http://dir.yahoo.com/Education/K-12/Newspapers/Individual_School_Papers/

Yahoo! Individual School Papers features links to student-produced online newspapers that teachers and children can use as a guide to improving their own school's publications.

Language Arts

A to Z Teacher Stuff's Online Collection

http://atozteacherstuff.com/lessons/

A to Z Teacher Stuff provides more than 500 language arts lesson plans and activities arranged by grade level for preschool and grades K-12. The site includes a search tool with language arts and thematic units categories.

Academy Curriculum Exchange

http://ofcn.org/cyber.serv/academy/ace/

The **Academy Curriculum Exchange** offers lesson plans covering various subject areas for grades K-12. To find more than 90 plans for language arts, click these links: Elementary School, Intermediate School, or High School.

ACCESS INDIANA Teaching & Learning Center

http://tlc.ai.org/

The **ACCESS INDIANA Teaching & Learning Center** provides a collection of language arts lesson plans for grades K-12. To find them, click on Teacher Lesson Plans in the Language section.

Activity Search

http://www.eduplace.com/search/activity2.html

Activity Search from Houghton Mifflin, features a curriculum database where K-8 teachers can search for language arts lesson plans/activities and other subject areas by grade level. Activities can also be browsed by theme.

ALI Units of Practice

http://ali.apple.com/ali/

The **Apple Learning Interchange (ALI)** contains lessons (units of practice) created by teachers for integrating technology into the teaching and learning process for grades K-12. Click on Units of Practice and use the "subject" and "level" pull-down menus to find language arts lessons for English or literature. You can search also by State & National Standards and the Resources section to find language arts lesson plans as well as participate in an ongoing collaborative projects sponsored by Apple.

AskERIC Lesson Plans

http://ericir.syr.edu/Virtual/Lessons/Lang_arts/

AskERIC Lesson Plans: Language Arts provides a collection of more than 100 language arts lesson plans contributed by teachers for grades K-12. Links include Literature, Writing Composition, Reading, and Spelling. Each lesson plan features an overview, purpose, objectives, activities, and resource materials.

Awesome Library: Language Arts Lesson Plans

http://www.awesomelibrary.org/Library/
Materials_Search/Lesson_Plans/
Language_Arts.html

The **Awesome Library: Language Arts Lesson Plans** contains a collection of hundreds of language arts lesson plans for grades K-12.

Bigchalk.com

http://www.bigchalk.com

Bigchalk.com provides a vast searchable collection of language arts and literature lesson plans arranged by grade level and topic or grades K-12. Click on Teachers and browse the lesson plan archives to find them.

Books@Random: Teacher Services

http://www.randomhouse.com/teachers.html

Random House provides a collection of teacher's guides for each of its separate divisions: Teachers@Random Resource Center for K-12; Junior-Senior High Teachers; and Random House Academic Marketing for grades 9-12. Each guide contains background story information, discussion and comprehension questions, and for grades 6-12, related research topics.

CanTeach Elementary Resources

http://www.track0.com/canteach/elementary/elementary.html

Iram Khan & James Hörner's **CanTeach** provides hundreds of elementary resources including English language arts lesson plans, songs and poems for use on special days and events, and information lessons. The site also includes thousands of English Language Arts sites on the main page offering tons of lesson ideas.

Carol Hurst's Children's Literature Site

http://www.carolhurst.com/titles/featuredtitles.html

Carol Hurst's Children's Literature Site contains a collection of lessons and activities to accompany more than 40 children's books. To see what's available at this site, click on Expanded Table of Contents on top of the page.

CEC Lesson Plans

http://www.col-ed.org/cur/

CEC Lesson Plans, sponsored by the Columbia Education Center in Portland, Oregon, features a wide variety of lesson plans created by teachers for use in their own classrooms. To find language arts plans to fit your needs, scroll to Language Arts and click Elementary (K–5), Intermediate (6–8), or High School (9–12).

Cinderella Stories

http://www.acs.ucalgary.ca/~dkbrown/cinderella.html

Cinderella Stories contains lesson plans with multicultural versions of Cinderella for grades 3–7. Scroll to Teaching Ideas by Jean Rusting where you'll find plans for Tattercoats, Cap o' Rushes, The Twelve Months, and The Princess and the Golden Shoes. You can also print a copy of these different versions.

Collaborative Lesson Archive

http://faldo.atmos.uiuc.edu/CLA/

Collaborative Lesson Archive, created by Bill and Dee Chapman, is a forum for the creation, distribution, and archival of education curricula for all grade levels and subject areas. To find language arts lesson plans for each grade level, click the grade level you want and then select either Reading or Writing. You can also submit a lesson plan.

Connecting Students

http://www.connectingstudents.com/

Connecting Students, maintained by David Leahy, provides a collection of Internet-ready lesson plans for grades K-12. Teachers will find language arts plans in the lesson plans, themes, Web lessons, and literacy sections.

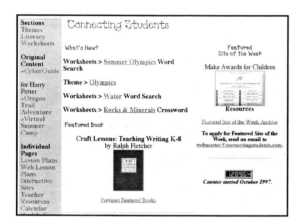

Connections+

http://www.mcrel.org/resources/plus/lang

McREL's **Connections+** provides a collection of lesson plans and activities for grades K–12. Click Language Arts, where you'll find plans for a variety of topics. The site also offers Haiku resources in the Multi/Interdisciplinary section.

Curriculum Guide for the Elementary Level: English Language Arts

http://www.sasked.gov.sk.ca/docs/ela/ela.html

The Saskatchewan Department of Education provides a curriculum guide with more than 50 lessons for teaching English language arts in grades 1-5. For an overview of the teaching strategies, scroll to Instruction, and to find the individual lessons, scroll to Sample Units.

CyberGuides: Teacher Guides & Student Activities

http://www.sdcoe.k12.ca.us/score/cyberguide.html

CyberGuides: Teacher Guides & Student Activities, from the SCORE Language Arts Project, are supplementary teacher-developed units based on more than 150 core works of literature, designed for students to use with the World Wide Web. Each CyberGuide, organized by grade level, contains a student and teacher edition, objectives, a task, and a process by which it may be completed. A rubric for assessing the quality of the student's work is also included.

EDSITEment

http://edsitement.neh.fed.us/

EDSITEment, a joint project of the National Endowment for the Humanities, the Council of the Great City Schools, MCI Communications Corp., and the National Trust for the Humanities, contains online lesson plans for teaching English, history, art history, and foreign languages at the high school level. To find them, click Lesson Plans.

Educate the Children: Literacy Lesson Plans

http://www.educate.org.uk/teacher_zone/classroom/literacy/index.htm

Educate the Children contains hundreds of K-12 lesson plans and worksheets, contributed by teachers, covering all phases of the English language arts curriculum.

Education World: Language Arts Lesson Plan Resources

http://db.education-world.com/perl/browse?cat_id=1874

Education World, sponsored by American Fidelity Services, provides a list of sites with more than 250 lesson plans covering the language arts curriculum for grades K-12. For additional lesson plans submitted by teachers, click on Teacher Lessons and find language arts in the Arts & Humanities section.

Encarta Lesson Collection

http://www.encarta.msn.com/schoolhouse/menus/menulangarts.asp

Encarta Lesson Collection offers hundreds of language arts lesson plans contributed by K-12 teachers.

The English Room

http://members.tripod.com/the-english-room/

The **English Room**, created by teacher Marsha Rogers, offers 30 days of poetry, a series of creative-writing lessons for students in grades 6 to 12. Students can use the pages to learn how to write poetry on their own, or the lessons can be used in a classroom setting. Student-written examples are provided for each lesson. A Teacher Page includes a list of materials needed, tips for using the lessons, and alignment to national standards. The final lesson includes a slide-show presentation with detailed instructions for creating a chapbook of poetry.

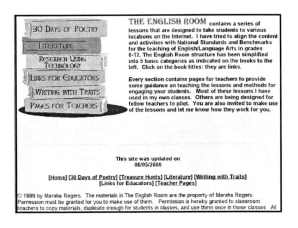

Fairy Tales from Far Off Lands

http://www.richmond.edu/~ed344/webunits/fairytales/title.html

Fairy Tales from Far Off Lands feature a collection of Internet-based lesson plans for studying fables around the world for grades 4-6. Places and countries covered include Africa, central Asia, China, Egypt, England, Native American, Russia, and Scotland.

Free Exemplary Lesson Plans

http://www.indiana.edu/~eric_rec/bks/lessons.html

Free Exemplary Lesson Plans, from ERIC Clearinghouse on Reading, English, and Communication, is a collection of K-12 language arts lesson plans taken from ERIC publications.

Gateway to Educational Materials

http://www.thegateway.org/

The **Gateway**, sponsored by the U.S. Department of Education, provides access to hundreds of lesson plans, curriculum units, and other education resources on the Internet for grades K-12. To find a collection of language arts plans, select Browse Subject Lists and click on Language Arts.

Gryphon House

http://www.ghbooks.com/

Gryphon House provides hundreds of language arts learning activities for preschool and the primary grades from books published by the company. To find these materials, select Get Free Activities! and scroll to Activity Books or Language Arts.

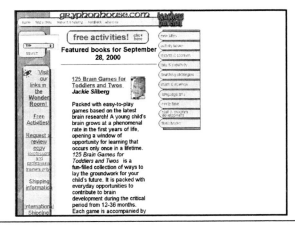

Jan Brett's Home Page

http://www.janbrett.com/

Jan Brett's Home Page, from the well-known picture book author and illustrator, provides 975 primary grade activities pages with classroom lessons in Newsnotes and Piggybacks sections. Students can make animal masks, use color pages, work on fun projects, read the "all abouts," and view lovely drawings. They can also send an electronic postcard from Brett's collection of more than 40 cards.

Kevin's Lesson Center

http://www.cbv.ns.ca/sstudies/lesson/lesson.html

Kevin's Lesson Center features a collection of lesson plans contributed by teachers for grades 4-12. The site includes English/language arts plans.

KidReach: Lesson Plans and Activities

http://www.westga.edu/~kidreach/lessons.html

KidReach: Lesson Plans and Activities provides unit lesson plans contributed by student teachers for teaching literature in grades 4-12. The site includes unit plans for the following books and plays: *Spirit Quest* by Susan Sharpe, *Daniel's Story* by Carol Matas, *Macbeth* and *Romeo and Juliet* by William Shakespeare, and *Night* by Elie Wiesel.

Kodak: Lesson Plans

http://www.kodak.com/edu/lessonPlans/

Kodak: Lesson Plans is a collection of lesson plans that combine photography and various curricular areas for grades K-12. The site includes nearly 60 lesson plans for language arts and English. All the plans require a camera.

Language Arts

http://www.sitesforteachers.com

Language Arts, from the Sharp's Web Sites and Resources for Teachers, is one of the most comprehensive sites for lesson plans and other language arts resources. The site contains thousands of lesson plans, a number of online student activities, and hundreds of literature links for grades K-12.

Learning Activities Archive

http://www.score.kaplan.com/activities/archive.html

Learning Activities Archive, from Kaplan's SCORE, provides a collection of lessons for various curriculum areas. Language arts topics include reading, vocabulary, grammar, creative writing, poetry, and writing a report.

Learning Resources

http://literacynet.org/cnnsf/

Learning Resources is a collection of weekly online interactive lessons using CNN news stories edited for easier reading for students in grades 6-12. The interactive lessons for each news story include curriculum exercises to test comprehension.

Lesson Plans From National Core Knowledge Conferences

http://www.coreknowledge.org/CKproto2/resrcs/

Lesson Plans From National Core Knowledge Conferences is a collection of units and lesson plans developed by teachers in Core Knowledge schools for grades PreK-8. The collection contains integrated plans for a variety of subjects, including language arts.

Lesson Plans From the Teacher's Desk

http://www.knownet.net/users/Ackley/lessons.html

Lesson Plans From the Teacher's Desk is a collection of more than 100 of Angela Achley's lesson ideas and activities for teaching spelling, writing, English, reading, and vocabulary in grades 4-6.

A collection of over 100 lesson ideas for Spelling, Writing, English, Reading, and Vocabulary activities, with a few extras thrown-in, currently being utilized in a fifth- or sixth-grade classroom

LessonPlansPage.com

http://www.lessonplanspage.com/

Kyle Yamnitz's **LessonPlansPage.com** offers hundreds of lesson plans organized by subject and grade level for grades K-12. Teachers will find plans in the language arts and multi-disciplinary sections.

Lesson Stop

http://www.youthline-usa.com/lessonstop/

Lesson Stop, maintained by Therese Sarah, contains more than 500 sites with thousands of lesson plans for grades K-12. The site includes language arts plans organized by topic and grade level. Other plans, such as Spinning Tales, can be found in the L.S. Lessons section.

LETSNet: Lesson Plans

http://commtechlab.msu.edu/sites/letsnet/noframes/subjects/

LETSNet, from Learning Exchange for Teachers and Students Through the Internet, provides language arts lesson plan units for grades K-12. The units include Ellis Island, Essay Exchange, School Newspaper, What's in a Name?, and Holiday Explorations.

Library in the Sky: Lesson Plans

http://www.nwrel.org/sky/Library/Materials_search/Lesson_Plans/Lesson_Plans.html

The **Library in the Sky**, provided by Northwest Regional Educational Laboratory (NWREL), contains hundreds of language arts plans for grades K-12.

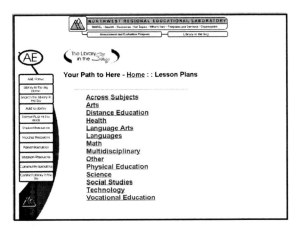

Lightspan.com: Lesson Plans

http://lightspan.com/teacher/pages/tools/default.asp?_prod=LS&_nav=t2_tools

Lightspan.com provides an extensive collection of traditional and collaborative lesson plans for PreK-12. To find language arts plans, click Lesson Plans.

Lesson Plan Database

http://humanities.byu.edu/linguistics/lp/home.html

Lesson Plan Database, created by Brigham Young University students, features a variety of language arts plans, including reading, writing, and grammar, for grades 7-12.

Link-to-Learn Classroom Activities

http://l2l.org/pd/tch_classroom.html

Link-to-Learn, an initiative of the Commonwealth of Pennsylvania, contains a collection of hundreds of Internet-enriched lesson plans and activities contributed by teachers for the elementary school, middle school, and high school. Language arts teachers can find classroom activities by title or grade level. Each classroom activity includes a plan to organize and structure the lesson, an activity worksheet that can be used online or printed for use as a handout, and extension tips with related sites for the lesson.

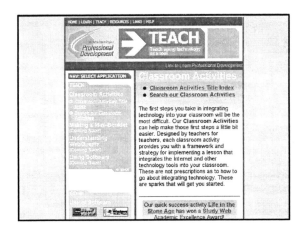

McDougal Littell's Language Arts

http://www.mcdougallittell.com/lit/

McDougal Littell provides teaching guides to more than 40 novels from *Animal Farm* to *To Kill a Mockingbird* for grades 6-12. The site also includes short biographical information about the authors.

McDougal Littell's Spelling Lessons

http://www.mcdougallittell.com/lit/liactspe.htm

McDougal Littell provides online 96 spelling lessons for grades 6 -8 that can supplement any middle school language arts curriculum. Each lesson includes a teacher's page and a student's page.

McREL: Language Arts Lesson Plans

http://www.mcrel.org/resources/links/langartslessons.asp

McREL: Lesson Plans and Activities, compiled by the Mid-Continent Regional Educational Laboratory, contains a collection of language arts lesson plans for grades K-12

Outta Ray's Head: Lesson Plans

http://www.cgocable.net/~rayser/lessons3.htm

Outta Ray's Head, maintained by high school English teacher Ray Saitz, features a collection of more than 125 lesson plans with handouts for teaching poetry, literature, writing, and library skills in grades 7-12.

Penguin Putnam: Teacher's Guides

http://www.penguinputnam.com/academic/resources/guides/

Penguin Putnam, suitable for high school English classes, provides Teachers' Guides for a variety of Signet classics. These printable guides contain ready-to-use lesson plans, discussion questions, and chapter-by-chapter and scene-by-scene breakdowns of numerous books used in high school English classes. For another source of plans, click Readers' Guides in the Classics section.

Primary Resources

http://www.primaryresources.co.uk/english/english.htm

Primary Resources offers hundreds of lesson plan ideas and worksheets for primary grade English language arts instruction.

Read In: Lesson Plans

http://www.readin.org/Educator/Lessons/main.htm

The **Read In Foundation** provides literacy-based, teacher-tested lesson plans aligned to California standards for grades K-12.

RHL School's Free Worksheets

http://www.rhlschool.com/

RHL School provides printable worksheets to complement language arts programs in grades 4-8. You'll find a collection of worksheets for English basics, reading comprehension, and reference skills. Teachers can request a free answer key that is updated weekly and sent by e-mail.

Scholastic Lesson Plans & Reproducibles

http://teacher.scholastic.com/lessonrepro/

Scholastic provides a collection of teacher-tested lesson plans, ready-to- use reproducible activities, and recommended Web sites for language arts topics in grades 1-8. The worksheets can be used independently of Scholastic materials and have answer keys.

School Express Free Worksheets

http://www.schoolexpress.com/fws/

School Express provides hundreds of free recopyable worksheets with answer sheets for phonics, sentence writing, handwriting, reading, and other language arts topics for grades PreK-8.

Schoolhouse: English and Language Arts

http://teacherpathfinder.org/School/english.html

Schoolhouse: English and Language Arts, part of Teacher/Pathfinder, provides a collection of English/language arts lesson plans for reading and writing in grades K-12. You can also search the site for lesson plans.

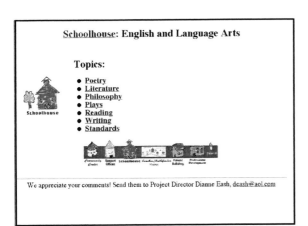

Scripps Howard National Spelling Bee

http://www.spellingbee.com/studyact.htm

Scripps Howard National Spelling Bee offers an entire year's worth of vocabulary activities, tips, and spelling lessons for grades 4-8. To find this material, click Mrs. Brooks' Lesson Plans and Carolyn's Corner in the Study Activities and Tips section.

The Shakespeare Corner

http://www.lausd.k12.ca.us/lausd/resources/shakespeare/Shakespeare.Corner.html

The Shakespeare Corner, created by Joel Littauer, contains lesson plans for teaching units on William Shakespeare's *Romeo and Juliet* in grade 9, *Julius Caesar* in grade 10, and *Hamlet* in grade 12. Each unit includes a teacher's guide, online student activities, and links to related sites.

The Story Arts

http://www.storyarts.org/

The Story Arts, created by children's author Heather Forest, provides a collection of storytelling lesson plans and activities for the elementary school language arts curriculum.

Surfing with the Bard: Lesson Plans

http://www.ulen.com/shakespeare/teachers/lessons/lessons.html

Amy Ulen provides more than 40 lesson plans for teaching Shakespeare to high school classes. Included are plans for *Hamlet, As You Like It, Macbeth, A Midsummer Night's Dream, Romeo & Juliet,* and other plays.

TeachersFirst Web Content Matrix

http://www.teachersfirst.com/matrix-f.htm

TeachersFirst Web Content Matrix, provided by the Network for Instructional Television (NITV), offers a collection of lesson plans at the elementary, middle, and high school levels. To find language arts plans, scroll to "Literature & Reading" or "Writing" in the table, and click on lesson plans.

Teacher Guide!

http://www.cagle.com/teacher/

Teacher Guide! features online lesson plans that use an extensive collection of current editorial cartoons from newspapers around the country. The site includes plans with printable student handouts for elementary school, middle school, and high school students in various subject areas, including English and journalism.

Teacher Talk Forum

http://education.indiana.edu/cas/ttforum/lesson.html

Teacher Talk Forum, sponsored by the Center for Adolescent Studies at the Indiana University School of Education, provides a collection of electronic lesson plans covering a variety of topic areas for grades 7–12. To find language arts plans, scroll and click Language Arts.

Teachers Helping Teachers

http://www.pacificnet.net/~mandel/LanguageArts.html

Teachers Helping Teachers offers language arts lesson plans for grades 2-12.

Teachers.Net Lesson Bank

http://teachers.net/lessons/

The **Teachers.Net Lesson Bank,** a curriculum exchange for grades PreK-12, provides a searchable collection of more than 500 lesson plans and activities contributed by teachers. To find language arts lesson plans, click on Reading/Writing or Literature on the left side or Curricula at the top of the page.

Teachervision.com's Lesson Plan Finder

http://www.teachervision.com/tv/curriculum/lessonplans/

Teachervision.com, part of the Learning Network, provides an extensive collection of lesson plans for PreK -12. To find language arts plans, use the grade level and the subject pull down menus.

Teaching Ideas for Primary Teachers

http://www.teachingideas.co.uk/

Teaching Ideas for Primary Teachers, created by Mark Warner, contains a collection of English and time-filler activities to complement a K-5 language arts curriculum. The site also includes worksheets which can be printed and photocopied for classroom use.

Teaching N' Technology

http://twister.coedu.usf.edu/tnt/

Teaching N' Technology (TNT), is a database of more than 400 technology-related lesson plans developed by Florida teachers for grades 4–12. The site includes plans for language arts as well as other subject areas matched to Florida's Sunshine State Standards. Each lesson plan contains computer and subject information and provides detailed instructions on how to implement the lesson in your classroom. You can search for plans by subject area, grade level, and keyword.

Teaching Shakespeare

http://www.folger.edu/education/

Teaching Shakespeare, sponsored by the Folger Shakespeare Library in Washington, DC, contains a collection of lesson plans contributed by classroom teachers or grades 8-12. The plans cover a variety plays and ideas.

Teachnet.com's Language Arts Plans

http://teachnet.com/lesson/

Teachnet.com, designed by teachers for K-12 teachers, offers language arts lesson ideas for reading writing, terminology, and general areas.

TEAMS Distance Learning: K-12 Lesson Plans

http://teams.lacoe.edu/documentation/places/lessons.html

TEAMS Distance Learning: K-12 Lesson Plans, maintained by the Los Angeles County Office of Education, provides a collection of lesson plan sites for grades K-12 organized by subject. To find language arts lesson plans, click Language Arts. You'll also find more language arts plans in the Multi-Subject Lesson Plans collection.

Tried *n* True Model Lesson Plans

http://www.teachers-connect.net/TNT/

Tried *n* True, from the North Carolina Department Public Instruction, is a collection of K-12 lesson plans contributed by teachers for a variety of subject areas. To find language arts plans, select a grade level and click the English Language key Arts in the table.

World School: Lesson Plans

http://www.wvaworldschool.org/html/lesson/lplans/lplans.htm

The **World School**, created by the West Virginia Department of Education, provides a collection of Internet-based lesson plans developed by teachers for grades K-12. Among the lesson plans are language arts, including an alphabetical list of literature units.

The Write Site

http://www.writesite.org/

The Write Site, developed by Greater Dayton Public Television for the middle school language arts curriculum, has students take the role of reporters and editors to research, write, and publish their own newspaper. The site includes unit outlines, student handouts, exercises, information on how to write materials, and much more.

WritingDEN

http://www2.actden.com/writ_den/

WritingDEN provides interactive online reading, comprehension, and writing lessons for students in grades 6-12. Using RealAudio, students can hear words pronounced and sentences narrated. The site, updated weekly, includes a teacher's guide, an archive of more topics, a grammar guide in the tips-o-matic section, an e-mail word-of-the-day feature, and a message board where students can post their messages.

Yale-New Haven Teachers Institute

http://www.cis.yale.edu/ynhti/

The **Yale-New Haven Teachers Institute** offers a collection of hundreds of curriculum units for grades K-12 prepared by teachers attending summer workshops from 1978 to 1997. Many of the units include lesson plans, student handouts, and specific classroom ideas. You can find language arts units by clicking on Curricular Resources.

A&E Biography Find

http://www.biography.com/search/

A&E Television Networks provides a searchable and browsable biography database of more than 25,000 prominent persons. To find a biography, enter a name in the box or click on a letter in the alphabetical listing. The site, suitable for grades 5–12, also offers, on the top menu, classroom materials and games to accompany the biographies.

About.com's Mark Twain

http://marktwain.about.com/arts/marktwain/

About.com's Mark Twain, maintained by Jim Zwick, provides a wide-ranging compilation of material by and about Twain. To find classroom materials for grades 8–12, scroll and click Teaching and a list of all the site's featured topics, scroll and click Subject Library.

Absolutely Whootie: Stories to Grow By

http://www.storiestogrowby.com/

Absolutely Whootie: Stories to Grow By offers a collection of folk and fairy tales based on themes of human values for grades 3-7. At the end of each story, children can write about the what the story was trying to show them. Children answer online and they can click to see what other children had to say, too.

Academy of American Poets

http://www.poets.org/index.cfm

The **Academy of American Poets** Web site includes biographies and photos of more than 200 poets, and nearly 600 poems. You can also listen to many of the poems online.

Aesop's Fables

http://www.pacificnet.net/~johnr/aesop/

Aesop's Fables, created by John R. Long, contains an alphabetically arranged collection of more than 655 of these fables for grades 3–12. The site includes some RealAudio narrations, a moral for each fable, and also 127 Hans Christian Andersen fairy tales.

Aha! Poetry

http://www.ahapoetry.com/

Aha! Poetry provides a wide variety of online poetry resources for grades 4–12. Students can learn poetic forms such as cinquain, ghazal, haiku, renga, sijo, and tanka. They can also add lines or commentary to existing poems in Ann Cantelow's interactive poetry pages, or post their own poems.

All Shakespeare

http://allshakespeare.com/

All Shakespeare contains critiques, essays, and commentaries on William Shakespeare's plays, sonnets, and essays. The site is suitable for grades 7-12.

Animal Alphabet

http://www.maui.com/~twright/animals/alphabet.htm

The **Animal Alphabet**, created by Thomas Wright for primary grade students, is an online interactive book that has a rhyme and an animal picture for each letter of the English alphabet. Clicking an animal takes you to a page with an illustration, a couplet, and some information on the species shown, plus links to other pertinent sites.

Author Pages on the WWW

http://falcon.jmu.edu/~ramseyil/author.htm

Author Pages on the WWW provides a comprehensive collection of author sites, compiled by Inez Ramsey, for grades 6-12. Categories consist of general resources, poet pages, women authors, young adult authors, individual author pages, and women authors from Mexico.

Awesome Cyber Greeting Cards

http://awesomecards.com/

Awesome Cyber Greeting Cards provides a large catalog of free online greeting cards you can personalize and send by e-mail. Card categories include all occasions, holiday, award, birthday, thank you, kids, baby, and graduation. The site is suitable for students in grades 3-12.

Baker Street Connection

http://www.citsoft.com/holmes3.html

Baker Street Connection features a collection of 56 Sherlock Holmes short stories and four novels written by Sir Arthur Conan Doyle between 1887 and 1925. The site is suitable for grades 7-12.

Barr's English Class

http://www.capecod.net/~bbarsant/class/

Barr's English Class, created by Nantucket High School teacher Robert P. Barsanti, contains his own class handouts, student worksheets, creative writing, and essay tips as well as related sites for teaching more than 40 literary works in grades 9-12.

Bartleby.com

http://www.bartleby.com/

Bartleby.com features an electronic library of the major British and American authors. The site, for grades 7-12, includes references, poetry, biographical information, illustrations, and online versions of the authors' works.

The Book Review Forum

http://faldo.atmos.uiuc.edu/BOOKREVIEW/

The Book Review Forum, created by Bill Chapman for elementary school students, features a list of book reviews written by students for other students. Students rate books they really want to read! To send a review, students can click Submit a Book Review and follow the online directions. They can also post a follow-up to a book already reviewed.

Children's Haiku Garden

http://www.tecnet.or.jp/~haiku/

Children's Haiku Garden contains haiku verses with illustrations from Japanese children and other children around the world. The site is suitable for grades 3-12.

The Children's Literature Web Guide

http://www.acs.ucalgary.ca/~dkbrown/

The Children's Literature Web Guide, maintained by David K. Brown, is one of the premier comprehensive resources for teaching children's literature in the elementary school. The site provides online children's stories, general children's literature resources, book awards, teacher resources, links to individual author sites, and much, much more.

ClueMaster

http://www.cluemaster.com/

ClueMaster, a free subscription service for grades 5-12, offers a collection of hundreds of crossword puzzles, word searches, and other word games that can be printed from your browser. The 50 quick crosswords and word searches are suitable for younger students, while the more challenging cryptic crosswords are suitable for high school students. Each word puzzle includes a printable answer sheet.

Cool Word of the Day

http://www.edu.yorku.ca/~wotd/

Cool Word of the Day, presented by York University College of Education in Canada, is a good way for students in grades 5-12 to build their English vocabularies. The site provides a new word daily, its definition, and an archive of past words. You can also add a word to the list.

Dakota Meadows Eighth Graders' Mystery Stories

http://www.isd77.k12.mn.us/schools/dakota/mystery/contents.html

Eighth grade students at Dakota Meadows Middle School in North Mankato, Minnesota, have written short, two-minute mysteries. Use your wits and detective skills to solve these cases.

Debbie's Unit Factory

http://www.themeunits.com/

Debbie's Unit Factory contains a collection of cross-curricular units and online resources for enriching language arts teaching in the elementary school. Click Table of Contents to find a list of the theme units, including free sample material and online quizzes. To find topical and monthly links, click Sneak Peeks.

The Dickens Page

http://lang.nagoya-u.ac.jp/~matsuoka/Dickens.html

The Dickens Page, maintained by Mitsuharu Matsuoka, contains a vast collection of sites devoted to Charles Dickens for grades 9-12. Included are photos, biographical information, electronic texts, recreational and film information, and other resources.

Disney Books: Story Time

http://asp.disney.go.com/DisneyBooks/StoryTime.asp

Disney Books: Story Time offers children dozens of their favorite illustrated books that can be read online.

Edward Bonver's Poetry Lovers' Page

http://www.poetryloverspage.com/

Edward Bonver's Poetry Lovers' Page provides the complete poetry collections of Edgar Allan Poe, Robert Louis Stevenson, and Rudyard Kipling, as well as selected poems of Aleksandr Pushkin, Aleksandr Blok, Anna Akhmatova, and others. The site, suitable for grades 6-12, also contains poems submitted by readers, and features links to a poem of the day and a random poem.

Emily Dickinson Random Epigram Machine

http://www.logopoeia.com/ed/

The **Emily Dickinson Random Epigram Machine** generates, every time you reload the page, a different Emily Dickinson poem. The poems are from *The Complete Poems of Emily Dickinson*, edited by Thomas Johnson and *New Poems of Emily Dickinson*, edited by William H. Schurr. The site is suitable for grades 7-12.

ePALS Classroom Exchange

http://www.epals.com/

ePALS Classroom Exchange, available in English, Spanish, or French for grades K-12, connects more than 65,000 classrooms (2.1 million students) from 182 countries around the world. You can search the site's database by school name, the classroom's first language, grade, the city/town, state/province, or country. You can then send an e-mail or visit the school's home page to find out if students there would like to become your students' pen pals.

The Encyclopedia Mythica

http://www.pantheon.org/mythica/

The Encyclopedia Mythica is an extensive encyclopedia of articles dealing with mythology, folklore, and legends from many of the world's cultures. It contains more than 5,700 definitions of gods and goddesses, supernatural beings, and legendary creatures and monsters. The site is suitable for grades 6-12.

The English Server

http://eserver.org/

The English Server, now located at the University of Washington in Seattle, is a cooperative that has been publishing humanities texts online since 1990. It offers more than 20,000 works covering a wide range of interests for K-12 language arts teachers.

ERIC/REC Clearinghouse

http://www.indiana.edu/~eric_rec/

ERIC/REC Clearinghouse is dedicated to providing reading, English, and communication (REC) educational materials, services, and coursework to anyone interested in the language arts. The site is suitable for grades K-12.

Fact Monster

http://www.factmonster.com/

Information Please provides **Fact Monster** for students grades 4-12. It is an encylopedia, a reference tool, and a homework helper just for children.

Fairrosa Cyber Library

http://www.dalton.org/libraries/fairrosa/

Fairrosa Cyber Library features an online reading room with bookshelves of classics, fairy tales and folk tales, and stories and rhymes for students in grades K-8. The site also contains a Lewis Carroll collection, an annotated list of dragon stories, an index to popular children's authors and illustrators, and related links to children's literature.

Fake Out!

http://www.eduplace.com/dictionary/

Fake Out!, provided by Houghton Mifflin for grades K-8, is a weekly definition guessing game in which a student selects a word from a grade-level list and tries to match it with its definition. The site includes answers, an archive of previous words, and teaching suggestions. Students can also choose one of next week's words, write their own fake definitions, and e-mail the definition.

Family Games Online Features

http://www.familygames.com/features.html

Family Games offers an online fantasy-adventure novel, randomly-generated haiku poems and stories (reload for a new versions), and other interactive features for grades 5-12.

Fluency Through Fables

http://www.comenius.com/fables/

Fluency Through Fables, presented by the Comenius Group, offers six fables for grades 5–12. Each fable is accompanied by interactive, self-correcting comprehension and vocabulary exercises.

FunBrain.com: Word Games

http://funbrain.com/words.html

FunBrain.com provides a wide variety of online language arts games for students in grades K-8. Word games include 2Bee or Nottoobee, Grammar Gorillas, Spellaroo. Wacky Tales, and Word Confusion. A great feature of the site is the free and easy-to-use Quiz Lab for teachers. Teachers can create their online quizzes for their students, or they can access hundreds of ready made quizzes prepared by other teachers. The sign-up form is a snap and takes less than a minute!

Grammar Now!

http://www.grammarnow.com/

Grammar Now!, answers any grammar, usage, composition, or editing question you have by e-mail. The site, suitable for grades 6–12, provides a convenient form to e-mail your questions and includes other useful grammar sites.

Grandpa Tucker's Rhymes and Tales

http://www.night.net/tucker/

Grandpa Tucker's Rhymes and Tales, updated monthly, features a collection of short, silly poems and online humorous stories written in verse for elementary school kids. The site also offers tips and materials for teaching poetry in the Family Fun Rhyme Time section. Teachers can print out the poetry to use in their own classrooms.

Great Literature Online

http://www.mostweb.cc/Classics/

Great Literature Online offers e-texts of famous authors from Louisa May Alcott to Walt Whitman accompanied by photos and biographical information. The site is suitable for grades 9-12.

Great Writers and Poets

http://www.xs4all.nl/~pwessel/writers.html

Great Writers and Poets, part of the Book Lovers home page, offers an alphabetized collection of prize-winning author sites as well as other author sites for high school English. Each author site includes a brief biography, short reviews of the major works, sample writings, a photo, and related links.

Grimm's Fairy Tales

http://www.cs.cmu.edu/~spok/grimmtmp/

Grimm's Fairy Tales, for grades K–5, provides a complete online collection of the 209 fairy tales written by the brothers Grimm. Translations are by Margaret Hunt.

Guide to Grammar and Writing

http://webster.commnet.edu/grammar/

Guide to Grammar and Writing, prepared by Charles Darling, is a comprehensive grammar reference for high school students. The site contains 170 computer-graded, cleverly animated quizzes that test a student's knowledge of grammar. Students can click grandma's rocker to Ask Grammar a question about punctuation, word usage, writing, or other related topics. A special form appears on which students can submit their questions. For hundreds of previously answered questions on grammar, click Grammar Logs.

Haiku-o-Matic

http://www.smalltime.com/nowhere/rhubarb/haiku.cgi

Haiku-o-Matic provides a new haiku poem at the click of the reload button. You can also submit your own or scramble the haikus.

Haiku-o-Matic

Haiku is a classical Japanese poetry form with a rich history, but this isn't a history lesson. The standard haiku format is a triplet of lines containing five, seven, and five syllables per respective line. When haiku is done well, it can be very good. You probably won't find any of that here. When haiku is done poorly, it can be very very bad. Select an option below to read or submit haiku.

Hans Christian Andersen Fairy Tales and Stories

http://HCA.Gilead.org.il/

Hans Christian Andersen Fairy Tales and Stories, compiled by Zvi Har'El for grades K–5, contains the complete list of Andersen's 168 stories in the chronological order of their original publication.

Home Page for Hamlet and Macbeth

http://www.webcom.com/falcon/

Home Page for Hamlet and Macbeth, sponsored by Falcon Education Link, makes the study of Shakespeare more enjoyable and understandable for high school students. Rodger Burnich, an English teacher, wrote the guides to *Hamlet* and *Macbeth*. The site also includes related Shakespeare links.

Index of Shakespeare Plays

http://www.unc.edu/~monroem/shakespeare/shakespeare.html

Index of Shakespeare Plays contains Matthew Monroe's summaries of plots for all 37 of Shakespeare's plays. Each summary covers the major developments and most of the important characters in the play. The material is useful for students in grades 7–12.

International Reading Association

http://www.reading.org/

International Reading Association (IRA) provides leadership in promoting literacy, improving the quality of reading instruction and teaching techniques, serving as a clearinghouse for the dissemination of reading research, and encouraging the lifetime reading habit. The site is suitable for grades K–12.

Internet Public Library's Shakespeare Bookshelf

http://www.ipl.org/reading/shakespeare/shakespeare.html

The **Internet Public Library** provides online the complete collection of all Shakespeare's plays. The site also includes links Webspeare study guides, a guide to Shakespeare's monologues, and other high school classroom resources.

Jane Austen Information Page

http://www.pemberley.com/janeinfo/janeinfo.html

Jane Austen Information Page, created by Henry Churchyard, is the premiere Austen site on the Internet. It contains six full-text, annotated versions of her novels, including an illustrated version of *Pride and Prejudice*. The site, suitable for high school English classes, includes articles on and by Jane Austen, numerous photos, information on the life and times of this celebrated author, online discussions of film and TV versions of her novels, and other related pages.

John's Word Search Puzzles

http://www.thepotters.com/puzzles.html

John's Word Search Puzzles, updated monthly, is a collection of more than 150 printable word searches for grades 3–8. Puzzle categories include Kids, States, Holidays, Sports, and TV/Movies.

Kid Crosswords and Other Puzzles

http://www.kidcrosswords.com/

Kid Crosswords and Other Puzzles, updated monthly, features a collection of more than 125 printable crosswords and other puzzles for grades 3–12. To find past puzzles for English, literature, and the holidays, click Previously Published Puzzles on bottom of page.

Kids' Books

http://www.scpl.lib.fl.us/kids/kids_booklists.html

The Seminole County Public Library System Services (SCPLS) in central Florida provides a collection of recommended books for students in grades K–12. Categories range from scary stories to U.S. historical fiction. Students are invited to write a review of a book they've read on the list which will be published at this site. To read reviews sent in by other kids from all over the world, click on the Review Index.

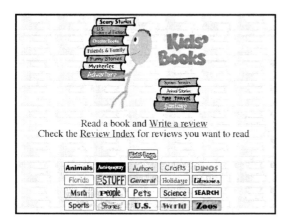

Kids' Space Connection: Penpal Box

http://www.ks-connection.org/penpal/penpal.html

Kids' Space Connection: Penpal Box provides a collection of penpal boxes that list kids who are looking for penpals by age group. There's a penpal box for ages 6 and younger, ages 7 and 8, ages 9 and 10, ages 11 and 12, and ages 13 through 16. For each child, you'll find the name, nickname, e-mail address, age, country, and short bio. There's also a class box for schools, an archive of the most recent penpal members, and a new search tool to help you find a penpal.

Learning Train

http://www.thepotters.com/ltrain.html

Learning Train features activities from Building Blocks to Reading, as well as other readiness reading ideas for students in grades PreK–2.

Literary Calendar

http://litcal.yasuda-u.ac.jp/

The Literary Calendar is an almanac of literary information in a this-day-in-history format. It contains a monthly calendar of events, allowing you to click a date to see what important literary events have occurred. You can also search for literary information by names, short phrases, or dates. The site is suitable for grades 8–12.

Little Explorers

http://www.littleexplorers.com/dictionary.html

Little Explorers is available in other language versions for preschoolers and elementary school students. It is an online picture dictionary with more than 1,650 entries and related Web sites. Click a letter in the alphabet to hear its pronunciation and to see a page of words that start with that letter.

Luminarium

http://www.luminarium.org/lumina.htm

Luminarium contains a selection of the major English authors and their works from the Medieval (1350-1485), Renaissance (1485-1603), and Early 17th-Century (1603-1660) periods. Each period includes an index of electronic texts, biographical information, beautiful images, a bibliography, essays and articles, and related sites. The site is suitable for high school AP English classes.

Merriam-Webster Online

http://www.m-w.com/

Merriam-Webster Online, suitable for students in grades 6-12, provides a dictionary where you can look up the meanings of more than 180,000 words and a thesaurus where you can find words with similar or opposite meanings. Other features include daily interactive word games, a word-of-the-day, and vocabulary builder.

Mr. William Shakespeare and the Internet

http://daphne.palomar.edu/shakespeare/

Mr. William Shakespeare and the Internet is an annotated guide to Shakespeare resources compiled by Terry A. Gray. Sections include information on Shakespeare's works, life and times, theater, criticism, and Renaissance sources. In addition, the Shakespeare in Education section provides a collection of teaching aids for middle and high school classrooms.

My Hero

http://www.myhero.com/

My Hero celebrates the "unsung" heroes among us by students to write about a very special person who has shown acts of courage, kindness, generosity, or ability. Students can also read about famous historical figures and ordinary heroes.

Nancy Keane's Booktalks — Quick and Simple

http://rms.concord.k12.nh.us/booktalks/

Booktalks—Quick and Simple, maintained by Rundlett Middle School in Concord, New Hampshire, is a database of more than 700 short booktalks for introducing books to students in grades K-12. You can view the short reviews by author, title, subject, or interest index.

Nathaniel Hawthorne

http://eldred.ne.mediaone.net/nh/hawthorne.html

Eldritch Press' **Nathaniel Hawthorne** home page contains extensive information on Hawthorne for high school students and teachers. The site includes electronic texts of Hawthorne's books and other writings, information about his life and work, and links to sites for other famous 19th-century American writers.

National Council of Teachers of English

http://www.ncte.org/

National Council of Teachers of English (NCTE), a professional organization for improving the teaching of English and language arts at all grade levels, offers, in the ideas section, practical teaching tips covering literature, reading, writing, and other topics submitted by teachers.

Novelguide

http://novelguide.com/

Novelguide is a massive online source for literary analysis of classic and contemporary literature. It includes more than 100 novel summaries, character profiles, metaphor analysis, theme analysis, top ten quotes, and author biographies, as well as a topic-specific literary search engine.

Nursery Rhymes

http://members.xoom.com/nur_rhymes/

Tracy Lightfoot provides online an alphabetical list of the traditional nursery rhymes that form a large part of our childhood experiences. Rhymes marked with an asterisk provide information about their origins or interpretations. The site is suitable for grades K–8.

The On-Line Books Page

http://digital.library.upenn.edu/books/

The On-Line Books Page, hosted by the University of Pennsylvania, is a searchable and browsable database to more than 11,000 online books and links to repositories of books. The site is suitable for grades 7–12.

PAL: Perspectives in American Literature

http://www.csustan.edu/english/reuben/pal/table.html

PAL: Perspectives in American Literature, created by Paul P. Reuben of California State University at Stanislaus, is an online research and reference guide to the major movements and authors in American literature. The site, suitable for AP English students, also provides research topics and study questions for every chapter in the guide.

PBS Kids

http://www.pbs.org/kids/

PBS Kids, for grades preK–5, contains a list of links to information on PBS TV kids' shows, including the time to watch them on more than 300 local PBS stations. The site also provides a wide variety of activities in the Fun & Games section, including coloring of more than 50 printable pages of favorite PBS characters.

Poetry for Kids

http://www.poetry4kids.com/

Poetry for Kids, for grades K–5, contains a collection of 40 wonderfully funny original poems written by Kenn Nesbitt. The site also includes links to other fun poetry pages.

Poets' Corner

http://www.geocities.com/~spanoudi/poems/

Steve Spandouis' **Poets' Corner** contains a collection of more than 6,200 poems by more than 600 poets categorized by author. The poems ranges from medieval English ballads to poems of the early 20th century. The site is suitable for grades K–12.

Purdue Online Writing Lab

http://owl.english.purdue.edu/

Purdue Online Writing Lab (OWL) features a collection of 150 handouts that students in grades 8–12 can use to improve their writing skills. Topics include punctuation, parts of speech, correct sentence structure, spelling, and research papers. To find these handouts, scroll to the bottom of the page. OWL also provides an extensive list of other Internet resources.

Puzzlemaker

http://puzzlemaker.com/

Discovery School provides an easy-to-use puzzle generation tool for teachers and students in grades 3-12. You can create and print customized word search, crossword, and other puzzles using your word lists. You can also build a maze or print our specialty hand-drawn mazes created around holidays and classroom topics.

Reader's Theater Editions

http://www.aaronshep.com/rt/RTE.html

Reader's Theater Editions provides 25 short scripts adapted from stories by Aaron Shepard and others. The material is mostly humor, fantasy, and retold tales from a variety of cultures. The site also provides tips on using the scripts. Teachers in grades 3–9 are encouraged to copy, share, and perform the scripts in their classrooms.

Reading/Language Arts at the Education Place

http://www.eduplace.com/rdg/

Houghton Mifflin's **Education Place** provides a collection of ready-to-use reading/language arts materials for grades K–8. "TeacherViews" contain reviews of favorite children's books and accompanied by classroom activities submitted by teachers, while the "Houghton Mifflin Spelling and Vocabulary" offers printable crossword puzzles and spelling exercises for each grade level.

SCORE Language Arts

http://www.sdcoe.k12.ca.us/score/cla.html

SCORE Language Arts, from Schools of California Online Resources for Education, is intended to reflect the California English Language Arts Framework for the K–12 curriculum. The site provides online student projects, lessons plans, teacher resources, and much more.

Sears Portrait Studio's I Can Do Avenue

http://www.searsportrait.com/icando/

Sears Portrait Studio's I Can Do Avenue provides wonderful language arts activities for grades PreK-2. Included are alphabet learning games, coloring pages, and nursery rhymes.

Shakespeare and the Globe: Then and Now

http://shakespeare.eb.com/shakespeare/index2.html

Encylopedia Britannica presents **Shakespeare and the Globe: Then and Now** featuring video and audio clips, including several animated views of the Globe Theatre and vintage audio and film clips of Shakespearean performances. The site is suitable for grades 8-12.

The Shakespeare Classroom

http://www.jetlink.net/~massij/shakes/

The Shakespeare Classroom, maintained by Professor J.M. Massi, features a variety of online resources for teaching Shakespeare in high school. The materials include study questions for more than 30 of Shakespeare's plays, answers to frequently asked questions about Shakespeare and his plays, information on the filmed versions of Shakespeare's plays, and links to related Shakespeare sites.

Shiki Internet Haiku Salon

http://cc.matsuyama-u.ac.jp/~shiki/

The **Shiki Internet Haiku Salon** introduces a new style of haiku poetry that has become popular in American schools. The site includes biographical information about Shiki Masaoka, anthologies of haiku, lessons on how to write haiku, and related links.

SparkNotes

http://sparknotes.com/

SparkNotes, created by Harvard University students and alumni, is a collection of free online study guides to approximately 100 literature classics for students in grades 6-12. Each guide contains sections on context, characters, overall summary, chapter-by-chapter summary and commentary, study questions, and a message board for collaborative learning. SparkNotes also provides guides for the works of Shakespeare and celebrated poets such as Donne, Dickinson, and Keats.

Story Creations

http://www.searsportrait.com/storybook/

Story Creations, provided by Sears Portrait Studio, is a collection of online, interactive stories that elementary school students can personalize by answering a few short questions. They can also print out or e-mail their stories to share with their classmates.

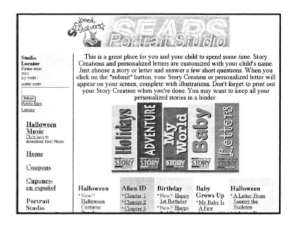

StoryFun!

http://www.mit.edu/storyfun/

StoryFun! contains online madlibs on a variety of topics. To create a hilarious story, choose a topic and type in funny verbs, nouns, and modifiers. Click the List of Story Topics to view the collection and click new story topic to reload for a new form. The material is suitable for students in grades 5-12.

Superteach

http://nz.com/webnz/checkers/free2.html

Superteach offers a collection of online, self-correcting language arts exercises for students in grades 6-12. Among these are the current grammar and proofreading lessons, with an archive of past grammar and proofreading lessons also available. The site includes exercises for improving a student's knowledge of idiom and slang and exercises for correcting writing mistakes.

SurLaLune Fairy Tale Pages

http://members.aol.com/surlalune/frytales/

The **SurLaLune Fairy Tale Site**, suitable for grades 4-8, contains a collection of annotated fairy tales, including historical and biograhical information.

Tales of Wonder

http://members.nbci.com/darsie/tales/

Tales of Wonder, compiled by Richard Darsie for grades 3-8, is a collection of more than 80 folk and fairytales from around the world. The stories provide insight about the traditions and feelings of many cultures.

TEAMS Distance Learning

http://teams.lacoe.edu/

TEAMS Distance Learning, from the Los Angeles County Office of Education, provides a wealth of online resources of interest to K-12 language arts teachers and students. Be sure to visit the Reading Village's Launching K-3 Readers Assessment Tools for teaching phonics.

University of Maryland Reading Room

http://www.inform.umd.edu/EdRes/ReadingRoom/

The **University of Maryland Reading Room** presents a comprehensive list of electronic texts from hundreds of classic fairy tales (fiction section) to the poems of William Butler Yeats and Elizabeth Barrett Browning (poetry section). The site is suitable for grades K-12.

Wacky Web Tales

http://www.eduplace.com/tales/

Wacky Web Tales, from Houghton Mifflin, asks students to fill in parts of speech to create wacky tales (madlibs) online. For a collection of previous tales, click More Tales by Dobie. The site also includes tales written by student writers. Students can also submit their own wacky tales by e-mail. The site is suitable for grades 3-8.

Wild World of Words Challenges

http://www.ash.udel.edu/ash/challenge/word.html

Wild World of Words Challenges provides a variety of interactive word games with which middle school students can improve their vocabulary, spelling, and grammar skills. Students can do online word scrambles, anagrams, and other word puzzles. They can also figure out crazy word combinations, learn new puns, and correct misspellings.

WillShakespeare.com

http://willshakespeare.com/

WillShakespeare.com contains everything on Shakespeare, including a quote of the week, a timeline, character profiles, quizzes, and complete texts of works. This site even offers an e-mail service for grades 7-12.

Words and Language

http://family.go.com/Categories/Activities/Features/
family_0401_02/dony/donytv_words/
donytv004.html

Words and Language, adapted from Steve and Ruth Bennett's book *365 TV-Free Activities You Can Do With Your Child*, contains an extensive collection of ready-to-use language arts activities for grades K–6. Among the activities are a backwards spelling bee, family historian, letter exchange, rhyming game, and wordgrams.

Wordsmyth English Dictionary-Thesaurus

http://www.wordsmyth.net/

The Wordsmyth English Dictionary-Thesaurus, developed at the University of Chicago, is an online English dictionary with a built-in thesaurus for grades 6–12. The site also includes the words-of-the week feature for ESL and college-bound students (SAT) as well as a variety of language tools in the Foundry.

Your Quotation Center

http://www.cyber-nation.com/victory/quotations/

Your Quotation Center, created by Cyber Nation International, features a searchable database of more than 43,000 quotes from famous people. You can view alphabetical lists of quotes by author or by subject. The site, suitable for grades 6–12, offers to send a daily quote by e-mail.

Mathematics

A to Z Teacher Stuff

http://atozteacherstuff.com/themes/math.shtml

A to Z Teacher Stuff provides hundreds of math lesson plans and activities arranged by grade level for preschool and grades K-12.

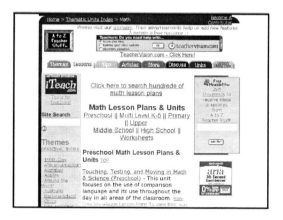

Academy Curriculum Exchange

http://ofcn.org/cyber.serv/academy/ace/

The **Academy Curriculum Exchange** offers more than 50 math lesson plans for the elementary school, the intermediate school, and the high school.

ACCESS INDIANA
Teaching & Learning Center

http://tlc.ai.org/

The **ACCESS INDIANA Teaching & Learning Center** provides a collection of math lesson plans for grades K-12. To find them, click on Teacher Lesson Plans in the Mathematics section.

AskERIC Lesson Plans

http://ericir.syr.edu/Virtual/Lessons/Mathematics/

AskERIC Lesson Plans provides a collection of math lesson plans contributed by teachers for grades K-12. Topics include Algebra, Applied Math, Arithmetic, Functions, Geometry, Measurement, and Probability. Each lesson plan features an overview, purpose, objectives, activities, and resource materials.

Applied Mathematics

http://www.bced.gov.bc.ca/careers/aa/lessons/math.htm

Lessons are linked to specific occupations encouraging students to see where math courses can take them in the real, working world.

ASPECT Activities

http://www.bgsu.edu/colleges/edhd/programs/ASPECT/activity.html

Bowling Green State University's Assessment Project for Erie County Teachers (**ASPECT**) provides a collection of lesson plans organized by grade level for grades K-12. Many of the plans include reproducible student worksheets.

Awesome Library:
Math Lesson Plans

http://www.awesomelibrary.org/Library/Materials_Search/Lesson_Plans/Math.html

The **Awesome Library: Math Lesson Plans** contains a collection of hundreds of math lesson plans for grades K-12.

Bigchalk.com

http://www.bigchalk.com

Bigchalk.com provides a vast searchable collection of math lesson plans arranged by grade level and topic. Click on Teachers and browse the lesson plan archives to find basic math, algebra, and geometry lessons for grades K-12.

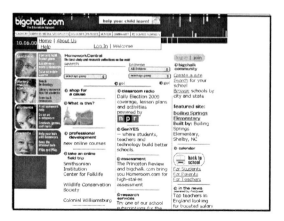

CanTeach Math

http://www.track0.com/canteach/elementary/
elementary.html

Iram Khan & James Hörner's **CanTeach** provides a variety of math lesson plans for grades K-6. Topics include numbers, patterns and relations, geometry, and probability.

CEC Lesson Plans

http://www.col-ed.org/cur/

CEC Lesson Plans, sponsored by the Columbia Education Center in Portland, Oregon, features a wide variety of lesson plans created by teachers for use in their own classrooms. To find math plans to fit your needs, scroll to Mathematics and click Elementary (K–5), Intermediate (6–8), or High School (9–12).

CEEE GirlTECH Lesson Plans

http://www.crpc.rice.edu/CRPC/Women/GirlTECH/
Lessons/

The Center for Excellence and Equity in Education (**CEEE**) provide a collection of more than 80 GirlTECH Internet-based lesson plans dating back to 1995. The lessons, contributed by teachers, cover a wide variety of math topics for middle and high school students.

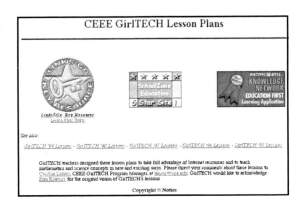

Conjectures in Geometry

http://www.geom.umn.edu/~dwiggins/
mainpage.html

Conjectures in Geometry from the University of Minnesota's Geometry Center contains interactive lessons featuring 20 conjectures found in typical geometry texts. Included in each conjecture are definitions, sketches and explanations, SketchPad demonstrations, and follow-up activities with solutions.

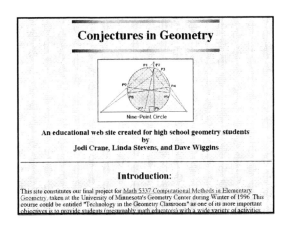

Connections+

http://www.mcrel.org/resources/plus/math/

Connections+ consists of Internet resources—lesson plans, activities, and curriculum resources provided by Mid-Continent Regional Educational Laboratory (McREL). K-12 math teachers can select from among these topics: Calculators, Patterns, Fractals, Computers, Functions, Algebra, and Polyhedra.

Cynthia Lanius' Mathematics Lessons

http://math.rice.edu/~lanius/Lessons/

Cynthia Lanius provides a collection of more than 20 math lessons the author developed for grades 6-12. Lessons include math puzzles as well as algebra and geometry problems.

Educate the Children: Numeracy

http://www.educate.org.uk/teacher_zone/class-room/numeracy/index.htm

Educate the Children provides a collection of hundreds of math lesson plans and worksheets contributed by teachers for grades K-12.

Education World: Math Lesson Plans

http://db.education-world.com/perl/browse?cat_id=1875

Education World: Math Lesson Plans, sponsored by American Fidelity Services, provides nearly 400 math lesson plans for grades K–12. Categories include Algebra, Applied Mathematics, Arithmetic, Geometry, Measurement, and Probability. For additional lesson plans submitted by teachers, click on Teacher Lessons and go to math in the left panel.

Eisenhower National Clearinghouse

http://enc.org/weblinks/lessonplans/math/

The **Eisenhower National Clearinghouse** at Ohio State University in Columbus, Ohio provides a wide variety of lesson plans for grades K-12. Topics range from counting to the Pythagorean theorem and functions.

Encarta Lesson Collection

http://www.encarta.msn.com/schoolhouse/menus/menumath.asp

Encarta Lesson Collection offers hundreds of mathematics lesson plans contributed by K-12 teachers.

Explorer

http://explorer.scrtec.org/explorer/

Explorer offers an extensive collection of math lesson plans and activities for grades K-12. Click the Mathematics Curriculum folder to find hundreds of plans on problem solving and reasoning, whole numbers and numeration, geometry, and other math topics.

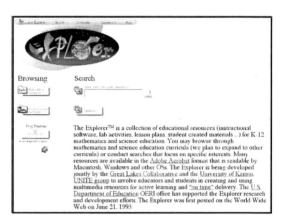

Forum Web Units and Lessons

http://forum.swarthmore.edu/web.units.html

Forum Web Units and Lessons is a collection of Internet-based projects with lesson materials for grades 6-12. Among the projects are Tom Scavo's "Adventures in Statistics and Tangrams," Richard Briston's "Tenth Grade Internet Math Assignments," Norman Shapiro's "Geometry Through Art," Jan Garner's "Perspective Drawing, Moebius Strip, Polyhedra, and Spreadsheets," and Suzanne Alejandre's "Polyhedra in the Classroom and Tessellation Tutorials."

Frank Potter's Science Gems— Mathematics

http://www.sciencegems.com/math.html

Frank Potter's Science Gems—Mathematics provides an exhaustive collection of K–12 lesson plans and activities sorted into 23 math categories.

Primary Resources

http://www.primaryresources.co.uk/maths/maths.htm

Primary Resources provides hundreds of lesson plan ideas and worksheets including math resources for the primary grades.

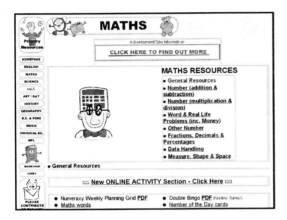

Gateway to Educational Materials

http://thegateway.org/

Gateway to Educational Materials, sponsored by the U.S. Department of Education, provides access to hundreds of lesson plans and curriculum units on the Internet for grades K-12. To find a list of math resources, select Browse Subject and click on Mathematics.

Good News Bears Stock Market Project

http://www.ncsa.uiuc.edu/edu/RSE/RSEyellow/gnb.html

Good News Bears Stock Market Project is an interdisciplinary unit specifically designed for middle school math students and teachers. It revolves around an interactive stock market competition in which students use real-time stock market data from the New York Stock Exchange and NASDAQ. The unit includes lesson plans and activities, reproducible pages, student handouts, and other related teaching materials.

Hands-on Math: Activities for the Elementary Classroom

http://www.xmission.com/~dparker/mathpage/handson.html

Janine Parker's **Hands-on Math Activities for the Elementary Classroom** contain classroom-tested lesson plans in geometry, number patterns, and topology. The geometry plans include step-by-step instructions for constructing the Platonic solids out of toothpicks and gumdrops.

Houghton Mifflin Activity Search

http://www.eduplace.com/search/activity2.html

Houghton Mifflin Activity Search features a searchable curriculum database where the K-8 teachers can find math lesson plans by grade level. Activities can also be browsed by theme.

Internet Mathematics Library

http://forum.swarthmore.edu/library/resource_types/lesson_plans/

The Math Forum provides hundreds of mathematics lesson plans selected from the Internet collections and individual author sites for grades K-12. The searchable and browsable collection is sorted by topic and grade level.

K-12 Statistics

http://www.mste.uiuc.edu/stat/stat.html

K-12 Statistics contains a list of Internet-based statistics lessons. The lessons include the following topics: NCAA basketball finals, earthquakes, minimum-maximum temperatures, weather plots, and temperatures.

KQED/CELL Math Lessons

http://www.kqed.org/ednet/school/math/mathonline/lessons/

KQED/CELL Math Lessons presents a series of cross-curricular math lessons organized by grade level for K-12 students and teachers.

LessonPlansPage.com

http://www.lessonplanspage.com/

Kyle Yamnitz's **LessonPlansPage.com** offers hundreds of lesson plans organized by subject and grade level for grades K-12. Teachers will find plans in the math and multi-disciplinary sections.

Lesson Stop

http://www.youthline-usa.com/lessonstop/

Lesson Stop, maintained by Therese Sarah, contains more than 500 sites with thousands of lesson plans for grades K-12. The site includes math plans organized by topic and grade level.

Link-to-Learn Classroom Activities

http://l2l.org/pd/tch_classroom.html

Link-to-Learn, an initiative of the Commonwealth of Pennsylvania contains a collection of hundreds of Internet-enriched lesson plans and activities contributed by teachers for the elementary school, middle school, and high school. Math teachers can find classroom activities by title or grade level. Each classroom activity includes a plan to organize and structure the lesson, an activity worksheet that can be used online or printed for use as a handout, and extension tips with related sites for the lesson.

Library in the Sky: Lesson Plans

http://www.nwrel.org/sky/

Library in the Sky, provided by Northwest Regional Educational Laboratory (NWREL), contains hundreds of math lesson plans for grades K-12.

Lightspan.com: Lesson Plans

http://lightspan.com/teacher/pages/tools/default.asp?_prod=LS&_nav=t2_tools

Lightspan.com provides an extensive collection of traditional and collaborative lesson plans for PreK-12. To find mathematics plans, click Lesson Plans.

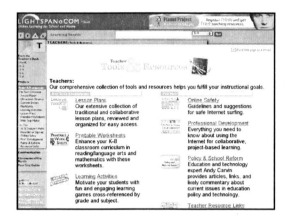

Math

http://www.csun.edu/~vceed009/math.html

Math from the Sharp's Web Sites and Resources for Teachers, contains a wide variety of math sites for lesson plans, online activities, and other math resources for grades K-12.

Math.com: Teacher Center

http://www.math.com/teachers.html

Math.com provides a collection of sites offering math lesson plans. Other useful resources include math references such as tables and glossaries in English and Spanish, as well as an online generator for algebra worksheets.

Mathematics Archives: K-12 Teaching Materials

http://archives.math.utk.edu/k12.html

Mathematics Archives: K-12 Teaching Materials contains extensive collections of lesson plans, activities, and other Internet resources for teaching K-12 math.

Mathematics Lessons Database

http://www.mste.uiuc.edu/html.f/k12.html

Mathematics Lessons Database, from the University of Illinois' Office for Mathematics, Science, and Technology Education (MSTE), provides a searchable database of more than 100 interactive math lessons involving real-life situations for high school students. You can also view the collection by scrolling to Browse the Entire Database.

McREL: Mathematics Lesson Plans

http://www.mcrel.org/resources/links/math/mathlessons.asp

McREL: Lesson Plans and Activities, gathered by Mid-Continent Regional Educational Laboratory (McREL), contains a collection of math lesson plan sites for grades K–12.

Mrs. Glosser's Math Goodies: Interactive Lesson Plans

http://www.mathgoodies.com/

Math Goodies features interactive math lessons, homework help, worksheets, puzzles, and message boards. The site offers more than 400 pages of free math activities and resources for teachers, students, parents, and homeschoolers.

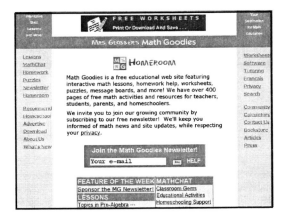

NCTM's Illuminations

http://illuminations.nctm.org/index2.html

The National Council of Teachers of Mathematics (**NCTM**) provides an array of standards-based math Internet lessons and ready-to-use interactive investigations developed by teachers for grades PreK-12.

New York Times Mathematics Lessons

http://www.nytimes.com/learning/teachers/lessons/mathematics.html

The *New York Times* provides lessons that let high school students see for themselves how math skills can improve their understanding of current events.

PBS TeacherSource

http://www.pbs.org/teachersource/math.htm

PBS TeacherSource offers an extensive collection of lesson plans for implementing standards-based instruction in grades PreK-12. To find these plans sorted by grade level, use the pull-down menu. The site also includes free online videos (PBS Mathline) showing teachers in actual classrooms around the United States.

Pi Mathematics

http://www.ncsa.uiuc.edu/edu/RSE/RSEorange/buttons.html

Pi Mathematics contains various resources for teaching students in grades 6–8 all about pi. The site includes lesson plans and activities, facts and history, projects, and applications.

SAMI: Math Resources

http://www.learner.org/sami/view-category.php3?category=math

Science and Math Initiatives (**SAMI**), sponsored by the Annenberg Foundation, contains hundreds of math resources for grades K–12. To find math lesson plans, click List, Search, or Browse.

Scholastic Lesson Plans & Reproducibles

http://teacher.scholastic.com/lessonrepro/

Scholastic provides a collection of teacher-tested lesson plans, ready-to-use reproducible activities and recommended Web sites for math topics in grades 1–8. The worksheets can be used independently of Scholastic materials and have answer keys.

School Express Free Worksheets

http://www.schoolexpress.com/fws/ sub_cat1math.asp?cat=Math

School Express provides hundreds of free recopyable worksheets with answer sheets for whole number computation, fractions, percents, and other math topics for grades PreK-8.

Schoolhouse: Mathematics

http://teacherpathfinder.org/School/math.html

Schoolhouse: Mathematics, part of Teacher/ Pathfinder, provides a collection of math lesson plans for grades K-12. Topics include arithmetic, algebra, and geometry. You can also search the site for lesson plans.

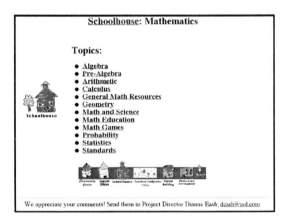

SCORE Mathematics Lessons

http://score.kings.k12.ca.us/lessons.html

The Schools of California Online Resource for Educators (**SCORE**) provides a collection of teacher-developed mathematics lesson plans for grades K-12 supporting the California Mathematics Standards. Other math plans are included in the yellow panel. All the lessons are organized by topic and by K-7 and 8-12 grade levels.

SMILE Program Mathematics Index

http://www.iit.edu/~smile/mathinde.html

The Science and Mathematics Initiative for Learning Enhancement (**SMILE**) program, maintained by the Illinois Institute of Technology, features almost 200 math lesson plans developed by teachers for grades K-12. Topics include arithmetic, geometry and measurement, patterns and logic, probability and statistics, recreational math, practical & applied math, graphs & visuals, and algebra & trigonometry. Each plan includes objectives, the materials needed, suggested strategy, and expected outcomes.

Susan Boone's Lesson Plans

http://www.crpc.rice.edu/CRPC/GT/sboone/ Lessons/lptitle.html

Susan Boone's Lesson Plans provides Internet-based math lessons and activities for grades 6–12. The activities include interactive projects in which students use math to solve real-life problems related to the Indianapolis 500, census data, real estate trends, and traffic reports.

Suzanne's Mathematics Lessons

http://forum.swarthmore.edu/alejandre/

Suzanne Alejandre provides a wide variety of original Web lessons she created to use with middle school math students. Topics include designs with circles, factoring through geometry, algebraic factoring, tesselations, creating magic squares, polyhedra, and fractals. Other math resources created by the author involve online interactive and classroom technology lessons.

Teachers Helping Teachers

http://www.pacificnet.net/~mandel/Math.html

Teachers Helping Teachers is a forum where K–12 teachers can share lesson plans in math and other subject areas.

Teachers.Net Lesson Bank

http://teachers.net/lessons/

The **Teachers.Net Lesson Bank,** a curriculum exchange forum for grades PreK-12, provides a searchable collection of more than 400 lesson plans and activities contributed by teachers. To find math lesson plans, click on Mathematics on the left side or Curricula at the top of the page.

TeachersFirst Web Content Matrix

http://www.teachersfirst.com/matrix-f.htm

TeachersFirst Web Content Matrix, provided by the Network for Instructional Television (NITV), offers a collection of lesson plans at the elementary, middle, and high school levels. To find mathematics plans, scroll to Mathematics in the table, and click on lesson plans.

Teachervision.com's Lesson Plan Finder

http://www.teachervision.com/tv/curriculum/lessonplans/

Teachervision.com, part of the Learning Network, provides an extensive collection of lesson plans for PreK-12. To find mathematics plans, use the grade level and the subject pull down menus.

Teaching Ideas for Primary Teachers

http://www.teachingideas.co.uk/

Teaching Ideas for Primary Teachers, created by Mark Warner, contains a collection of math and time-filler activities to complement a K-5 mathematics curriculum. The site also includes worksheets which can be printed and photocopied for classroom use.

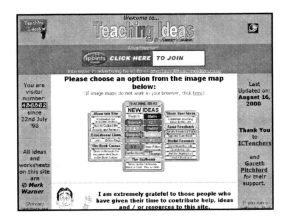

Teaching Mathematics in the Middle and Secondary Schools

http://euclid.barry.edu/~marinas/mat476/lessons.html

Teaching Mathematics in the Middle and Secondary Schools contains 40 lesson plans created by teachers from Florida that require minimum preparation. Most of the lessons are cross-curricular and involve math in practical and real-life situations.

Teaching N` Technology

http://twister.coedu.usf.edu/tnt/

Teaching N' Technology (TNT), is a database of more than 400 technology-related lesson plans developed by Florida teachers for grades 4–12. The site includes plans for mathematics as well as other subject areas matched to Florida's Sunshine State Standards. Each lesson plan contains computer and subject information and provides detailed instructions on how to implement the lesson in your classroom. You can search for plans by subject area, grade level, and keyword.

Teachnet.com's Math Plans

http://teachnet.com/lesson/

Teachnet.com designed by teachers for K–12 teachers, offers mathematics lesson ideas for geometry, maps and graphs, money, real world, terminology, and general areas.

TEAMS Distance Learning: K–12 Lesson Plans

http://teams.lacoe.edu/documentation/places/lessons.html

TEAMS Distance Learning: K–12 Lesson Plans, maintained by the Los Angeles County Office of Education, provides a collection of lessons plan sites for grades K-12 organized by subject. To find math lesson plans, click Mathematics.

This is MEGA Mathematics: Los Alamos National Laboratory

http://www.c3.lanl.gov/mega-math/

This Is MEGA Mathematics: Los Alamos National Laboratory provides seven innovative hands-on math lessons complete with activities and materials for grades 4-12. Select from among these topics: The Most Colorful Math of All, Games on Graphs, Welcome to the Hotel Infinity, and A Usual Day at Unusual School.

A+ Math

http://www.aplusmath.com/

A+ **Math** features an interactive game room where elementary school students can practice online their math skills. Students will find flashcard and advanced problem programs as well as hidden picture and concentration-like games. In addition, students can use a variety of homework tools to check their work.

AAA Math

http://www.aaamath.com/

AAA **Math**, designed by John Banfill for grades K-8, contains more than 200 pages of math exercises organized by grade level and topic. Each page includes detailed instructions, interactive demonstrations, and engaging activities that can improve your students' math skills.

AIMS Puzzle Corner

http://www.aimsedu.org/Puzzle/PuzzleList.html

The **AIMS Puzzle Corner**, online since 1995, contains a collection of challenging puzzles for students in grades K–8. Each puzzle includes a printable worksheet, and the solution for the current month puzzle appears the following month. A new puzzle page is added every month.

Allmath.com

http://www.allmath.com/

Allmath.com, sponsored by Arbor Media, provides a variety of interactive math resources for elementary school students to practice their basic facts online. It features math flashcards, multiplication tables, a magic square game, and a metric converter. The site also includes biographies of mathematicians and a glossary of math terms.

Ask Dr. Math

http://forum.swarthmore.edu/dr.math/dr-math.html

The Math Forum's **Ask Dr. Math** provides online math help for students in grades K-12. It includes an archive of hundreds of questions and answers. The site is divided into elementary school, middle school, and high school levels.

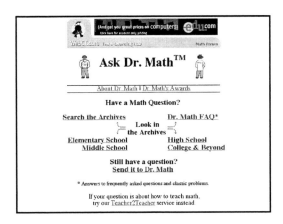

Aunt Annie's Crafts: Boxes and Bags

http://www.auntannie.com/boxbag.html

Aunt Annie's Crafts provides a variety of art projects useful for students learning geometry in grades 6-12. Students can make their own boxes and bags in different shapes, sizes, and designs.

Aunty Math's Fun Math Challenges for Kids

http://www.dcmrats.org/auntymath.html

Aunty Math from DuPage Children's Museum near Chicago posts every two weeks a math challenge in story form for elementary level students. Students can write in with their answers and get back comments from Aunty Math or others. The site also includes archives of past problems, tip sheets for teachers, as well as extensions to other subjects built into the stories.

Bamdad's Math Comics Page

http://www.csun.edu/~hcmth014/comics.html

Bamdad's Math Comics Page, frequently updated with new comics, features a collection of more than 200 cartoons scanned from newspapers and magazines. These cartoons, suitable for grades 5-12, usually involve humorous math-related situations.

BEATCALC: Beat the Calculator!

http://forum.swarthmore.edu/k12/mathtips/2digit5.html

The Math Forum provides more than 185 mental calculation shortcuts from B. Lee Clay's Beat the Calculator (**BEATCALC**) mailing list for grades 5-12. Each shortcut contains a clear explanation and a sample problem. For a list of all the shortcuts, scroll to the bottom of the page and click on Full List. The site includes practice problems to accompany these shortcuts. Teachers can subscribe via e-mail to this free weekly service.

Ben's Marvelous Mastermind Game

http://www.math.berkeley.edu/~bdavis/Mastermind/

Ben Davis, a graduate math student at the University of California, Berkeley, has created an online version of the Mastermind board game for students in grades 5-12. You try to guess the right combination of colors the computer has randomly selected. You can customize the number of colors, the board width, and other options for each game. There are 720 different online versions.

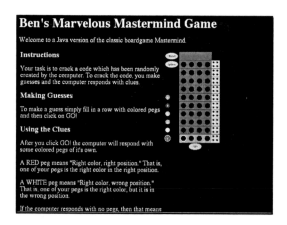

Biographies of Women Mathematicians

http://www.agnesscott.edu/lriddle/women/women.htm

Biographies of Women Mathematicians is part of an ongoing project by students in mathematics classes at Agnes Scott College in Atlanta, Georgia. Included are more than 150 biographies of women mathematicians illustrating their past and present achievements. The site, suitable for grades 6-12, also offers other math history links.

Brain Teasers

http://www.eduplace.com/math/brain/

Houghton Mifflin's **Brain Teasers** are provided weekly for students in grades 3–8. The teasers are organized by grade level, and answers appear the following week.

BU's Interactive WWW Games

http://scv.bu.edu/Games/games.html

Boston University Scientific Computing and Visualization Group provides a collection of online interactive board games students can play on their computers. Games include Pegs, Minesweep, 9 Puzzle, Triple Yahtzee, and WinFive.

Carol Hurst's Math and Children's Literature

http://www.carolhurst.com/subjects/math/math.html

Carol Hurst's Math and Children's Literature offers a variety of ways to integrate children's literature with math. The site provides ideas and activities from articles Hurst wrote for the *Teaching K-8 Magazine*. It also includes a list of recommended books by grade level and theme.

Clever Games for Clever People

http://www.cs.uidaho.edu/~casey931/conway/games.html

Clever Games for Clever People, adapted from John Conway's book *On Numbers and Games*, features 17 classroom logic or strategy games for improving the math abilities of middle school and high school students. Each game includes simple rules, a description of the necessary materials, and clear directions for creating the games.

Cool Math4Kids.com

http://coolmath4kids.com/

Cool Math features interactive games, puzzles, and online calculators for grades PreK-12. In Number Monster, children can play against the computer to practice the four operations of adding, subtracting, multiplying, and dividing. Kids 13+ will find lessons on geometry, trigonometry, calculus, and algebra, an area with puzzles and number games.

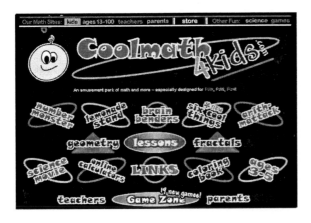

Connect!

http://www.pomakis.com/c4/c4.cgi

Connect! by Keith Pomakis provides kids in grades 3-8 with easy-to-follow rules and an attractive gameboard for playing this popular logic game on the Web.

Cyber School Resources

http://www.accessone.com/~bbunge/

Robert Bunge provides a WorksheetMaker which generates whole number practice worksheets that teachers can print and recopy for use with students in grades 2-6. In addition, he includes Interactive Algebra exercises which allows high school students to practice online equations, factoring, and graphing skills. There are multiple levels for each topic and exercise hints.

Dave's Math Tables

http://www.sisweb.com/math/tables.htm

Dave's Math Tables, available in both English and Spanish versions for grades 5-12, provides a vast array of math topics from a basic multiplication table to something as mind-boggling as a "Fourier series." It includes an English-Spanish Math Dictionary.

Desdemona

http://www.math.hmc.edu/~dmazzoni/cgi-bin/desmain.cgi

Dominic Mazzoni's **Desdemona** is an interactive online version of the classic game of Othello, also known as Reversi. You play against the computer on a board trying to outflank your opponent's discs. The player wins who has the majority of discs on the board at the end of the game. The site provides rules how to play the game.

Discovery School's WebMath

http://school.discovery.com/homeworkhelp/webmath/

Discover School's WebMath provides instant step-by-step solutions to your math problems from pre-algebra topics to calculus problems.

Eight Great Riddles

http://www.scottforesman.com/sfaw/resources/riddles/mathrid.html

Scott Foresman Addison Wesley provides online eight math riddles with accompanying answers for students in grades 3–7.

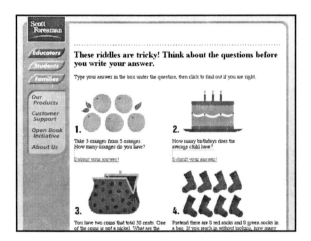

Famous Problems in the History of Mathematics

http://forum.swarthmore.edu/~isaac/mathhist.html

Isaac Reed presents a collection of some of the great problems that have inspired mathematicians from Zeno to Cantor suitable for middle school and high school math students. Included are solutions, as well as links to mathematicians' biographies and other math history sites.

Figure This! Math Challenges for Families

http://www.figurethis.org/

Figure This! provides math challenges around everyday situations for middle school students. Challenges cover questions related to health, transportation, food, and more. Each challenge includes fun statistics, related resources, and math resources for parents. For more entertaining math problems, click on Math Is Power at the bottom of the page.

Financial Calculators!

http://www.hsh.com/calculators.html

Financial Calculators!, maintained by HSH Associates, provides a variety of basic financial calculators that high school students can use to gain a better knowledge of money management strategies.

Finch Math Problems of the Week

http://www.mbnet.mb.ca/~jfinch/math.html

Mr. Finch offers his collection of weekly math problems for each month of the year. The site includes problems as well as answers for grades 3-6.

Flashcards for Kids

http://www.edu4kids.com/math/

Flashcards for Kids, sponsored by CANITech, provides a collection of interactive math flashcards for students in grades K-8. Students can practice online their basic math computations choosing the skill, the difficulty level, and the numbers to be used. The site also keeps score and informs students when their answers are wrong.

Forum Interactive Projects

http://forum.swarthmore.edu/mathsites/forum.html

The Math Forum provides a variety of Interactive Projects featuring online help, problems, and projects for students and teachers in grades 3–12.

FunBrain.com: Number Games

http://funbrain.com/numbers.html

FunBrain provides 14 math games for students in grades K-8 to play, including practice counting money, measurement, algebra, graphing coordinates, secret codes, order of operations, and fractions. These games let you customize problem difficulty, and offer tips if you give an incorrect answer. The money changing game allows you to play with money from five nations. Another great feature of the site is the free and easy-to-use Quiz Lab for teachers. Teachers can create their online quizzes for their students, or they can access hundreds of ready made quizzes prepared by other teachers. The sign-up form is a snap and takes less than a minute!

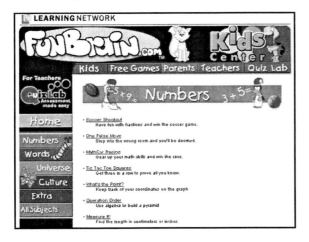

Fundrum My Conundrum

http://www.cataloguesonline.com/puzzles/

Fundrum My Conundrum features a collection of 100 riddles, puzzles, and conundrums organized by difficulty level for grades 4-12. Answers are provided.

Geometry and the Imagination in Minneapolis

http://www.geom.umn.edu/docs/doyle/mpls/handouts/handouts.html

Geometry and the Imagination in Minneapolis consists of more than 30 handouts for high school math students. Topics include knots diagrams and maps, geometry on the sphere, Descartes' formula, topology, and Gaussian curvature.

The Geometry Center

http://www.geom.umn.edu/

The Geometry Center at the University of Minnesota features COMAP teaching materials, a gallery of geometry explorations in Interactive Web Applications, and a variety of geometry projects, and for high school math students in the Course Materials section.

Geometry Junkyard

http://www.ics.uci.edu/~eppstein/junkyard/

David Eppstein's **Geometry Junkyard** contains a wide variety of attractively illustrated geometry articles for grades 9-12. Topics include circles and spheres, coloring, covering and packing, dissection, geometric models, knot theory as well as the author's own contributions.

Interactive Mathematics Miscellany and Puzzles

http://www.cut-the-knot.com/

Alexander Bogomolny provides a collection of hundreds of interactive activities and puzzles that illustrate mathematical concepts for high school students and teachers. Topics include games and puzzles, arithmetic, algebra, geometry, probability, proofs, "impossible" math topics, and others. Solutions and explanations are provided for each puzzle.

Interactive Web Games

http://genesis.ne.mediaone.net/games.html

Steve Belczyk provides four interactive Web games for students in grades 5-12. The games are WebBattleship, WebMinesweeper, WebReversi, and WebMaze.

Internet Math Challenge

http://www.uidaho.edu/LS/Math/imc/

The University of Idaho University provides a collection of math challenges and puzzles for K-12 students. The site includes puzzles with solutions from the 1999-2000 school year.

K-12 Math Problems, Puzzles, Tips & Tricks

http://forum.swarthmore.edu/k12/mathtips/

The Math Forum provides an extensive collection of math problems, puzzles, tips and tricks for grades K-12.

Lemonade Stand on the Web

http://www.littlejason.com/lemonade/

Jason Mayans' **Lemonade Stand on the Web** teaches basic business math (sales minus expenses equals profits) to children in grades 5-8. The object of the game is to make as much money as possible in 25 rounds. Before each round starts, you review the weather forecast. Then you decide how many cups of lemonade to make, and how much to spend on advertising. At the end of each round, you receive a summary of how many cups sold and how much profit you've made.

MacTutor History of Mathematics Archive

http://www-groups.dcs.st-and.ac.uk/~history/

The **MacTutor History of Mathematics Archive**, created by John J. O'Connor and Edmund F. Robertson of the University of St. Andrews in Scotland, features a collection of more than 1,500 biographies of mathematicians, with snapshots arranged in alphabetical and chronological lists. This site, suitable for grades 6-12, also includes birthplace maps, history topics, an index to female mathematicians, and related Web resources.

Mancala

http://imagiware.com/mancala/

Mancala is an ancient challenging African pit game (a.k.a. Kalaha) involving logic and strategy for grades 4-12. It includes simple rules to follow and a hint button that helps new players make good moves.

Math Education and Technology

http://www.ies.co.jp/math/indexeng.html

The Japanese company, International Education Software (IES), provides online a collection of more than 245 interactive, animated Java applet programs illustrating mathematical concepts for middle and high school students. The site, updated bimonthly, includes applets for geometry, trigonometry, calculus, and other math topics.

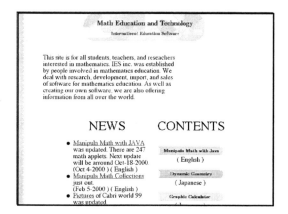

The Math Forum

http://forum.swarthmore.edu/

The Math Forum, sponsored by Swarthmore College, is a one-stop Internet guide for all your K-12 math needs. It features lesson plans, interactive activities, materials, and Web sites related to teaching arithmetic, algebra, geometry, and advanced math topics.

Math Pages

http://www.seanet.com/~ksbrown/

Kevin Brown's **Math Pages** is a treasure chest of information containing more than 300 articles on a variety of mathematical topics for teachers of advanced level math courses. Topics include number theory, combinatorics, geometry, algebra, calculus, differential equations, probability, statistics, physics, and the history of math.

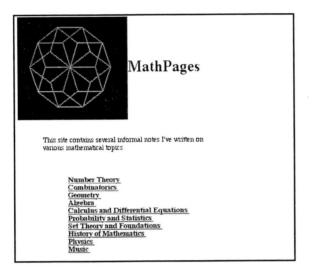

Math Parent Handbook

http://www.eduplace.com/math/res/parentbk/

Houghton Mifflin's **Math Parent Handbook** provides math games and puzzles to motivate elementary school students. To find the material, click on refrigerator math or quick and easy math games.

MathStories.com

http://www.mathstories.com/

MathStories.com features more than 4,000 ready-to-use worksheets with word problems for grades 1-8 organized by grade level. Topics include whole number operations, fractions, and decimals as well as magic with numbers, children's books, and thematic word problems.

Mathwork

http://www.coastlink.com/users/sbryce/mathwork/

Scott Bryce's **Mathwork** allows elementary school teachers to create and print math worksheets for addition, subtraction, multiplication, and division of whole numbers as well as for some fraction and measurement topics.

Monster Math

http://www.lifelong.com/programs/k12/math/mm/

Lifelong's **Monster Math**, available in English, Spanish, and Italian, is an online interactive, story for the primary grades. The site is designed to introduce and review a variety of basic math concepts such as counting, addition, and multiplication in which kids answer simple number questions about a monster to advance in the story.

National Council of Teachers of Mathematics

http://www.nctm.org/

The National Council of Teachers of Mathematics (NCTM) is the largest professional organization for improving the teaching of mathematics for grades K–12. To find classroom activities, visit Publications and Teachers Corner.

NRICH

http://www.nrich.maths.org.uk/

The University of Cambridge provides math enrichment for primary through high school students with a variety of problems, puzzles, animations, and games. There are explorations with LOGO for all age groups. New articles and problems are posted monthly but you can also view back issues.

Number and Word Puzzles

http://www1.tpg.com.au/users/puzzles/

Ken Egan provides many different types of puzzles he has created for students in grades 5-12. You will also find the solutions to the puzzles. All can be printed from your browser.

Northwestern Mutual's Longevity Game

http://www.northwesternmutual.com/games/longevity/

Northwestern Mutual's **Longevity Game** is an interactive lifestyle and health awareness quiz. It provides a means to calculate how long you can expect to live based on life insurance industry research. Everyone starts with the average life expectancy of 73 years and adds or subtracts years from the score as he or she responds to a questionnaire.

Open-ended Math Problems

http://sln.fi.edu/school/math2/

Gwenn Holtz and Mary Lee Malen, two math teachers at the Levering School in Philadelphia, have developed a collection of open-ended math problems for middle school students. For other math and logic problems also from these teachers, visit **http://sln.fi.edu/school/math/** and **http://www.fi.edu/sln/school/tfi/spring96/logic.html**.

Panthera's Puzzle Contest

http://www.puzzleu.com/pow/

Panthera's Puzzle Contest enables children in grades 4-8 to e-mail their solutions to 42 puzzles. You'll also find solutions to the previous 42 puzzles. To play grid-type logic games online, click Light Puzzles.

The Pi-Search Page

http://www.aros.net/~angio/pi_stuff/piquery.html

The Pi-Search Page, suitable for grades 8-12, helps students better understand irrational numbers. They can enter any number and determine its location in pi. For example, by choosing July 4, 1776, and entering 070476, students can find out where that set of numbers is in pi's unending sequence of digits.

The Prime Pages

http://www.utm.edu/research/primes/

The Prime Pages offer an extensive collection of material about prime numbers, including the sieve of Erastothenes, lists of prime numbers and factorizations, the Mersenne primes, and a general historical introduction to primes. The site is suitable for grades 9-12.

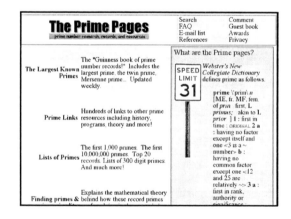

Principles and Standards for School Mathematics: Electronic Examples

http://standards.nctm.org/document/eexamples/

This electronic version of **Principles and Standards for School Mathematics**, published by the National Council of Teachers of Mathematics (NCTM), offers interactive animated activities organized by grade level that support the math standards.

Problem-of-the-Week Home Page

http://www.wits.ac.za/ssproule/pow.htm

Stephen Sproule provides a collection of problem-of-the-week sites organized by grade level for grades K-12.

The rec.puzzles archive

http://einstein.et.tudelft.nl/~arlet/puzzles/

The rec.puzzles archive, maintained by Arlet Ottens, contains tons of puzzles and brain teasers categorized by topic for grades 9-12. The puzzles were compiled from various sources, and each puzzle includes a solution.

RHL School

http://rhlschool.com/

RHL School provides weekly printable worksheets to complement any math program in grades 4-8. You'll find a collection of worksheets for computation and problem solving. Teachers can request a free weekly updated answer key sent by e-mail.

Saxon Online Math Activities

http://www.saxonpub.com/tech/online_activities.html

Saxon Publishers provide a variety of online math games and problems for grades K-12. The site includes interactive basic facts and multiple counting practice, a kindergarten pattern block game, and math enrichment and math stumper problems.

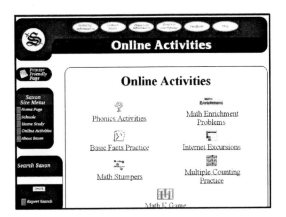

Shack's Math Problems

http://www.thewizardofodds.com/math/

Shack's Math Problems contains a collection of more than 155 math and logic problems ranging from basic math to differential equations. Each problem includes a difficulty rating, an answer, and usually a solution with an explanation. The site is suitable for grades 7-12.

S.O.S. MATHematics

http://sosmath.com/

S.O.S. MATHematics from the University of Texas at El Paso contains a wide variety of online worksheets for algebra, trigonometry, calculus, and other advanced math topics for students in grades 7-12. Each exercise includes a set of problems and answers giving clear explanations and appropriate practice so that a student is able to check his/her understanding and monitor his/her progress.

Sprott's Fractal Gallery

http://sprott.physics.wisc.edu/fractals.htm

Sprott's Fractal Gallery is suitable for grades 6–12. Every day, the site presents a new fractal that is automatically generated by the author, Julien C. Sprott. It contains an archive of previous fractals and links to thousands of fractal patterns from other sources.

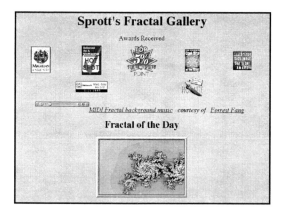

21st Century Problem Solving

http://www.hawaii.edu/suremath/home1.html

Howard McAllister's **21st Century Problem Solving** features the author's instructional approach to problem solving that applies across the curriculum and at all grade levels. The site provides numerous examples of problems solved using the author's problem solving methods, a discussion of the principles of reliable problem solving, and an evolving encyclopedia of solved problems in pre-college algebra, physics, and chemistry. For a list of all the solved problems, click Solved.

Teacher2Teacher

http://forum.swarthmore.edu/t2t/

The Math Forum's **Teacher2Teacher** is an online resource for K-12 teachers who have questions about teaching math. This service provides an archive of answers, pages of public discussions, and a form for submitting questions.

The Universal Currency Converter

http://www.xe.net/currency/

The Universal Currency Converter includes simple instructions that allow middle school students to perform interactive foreign-exchange-rate conversions on the Internet.

What Is a Dollar Worth?

http://woodrow.mpls.frb.fed.us/economy/calc/cpihome.html

The Consumer Price Index (CPI) measures the average level of prices of the goods and services typically consumed by an urban American family. The Federal Reserve Bank of Minneapolis maintains this site enabling middle and high school students to calculate the buying power of a dollar between 1913-1999. It also explains how the CPI is used to make the calculations.

Word Problems For Kids

http://www.stfx.ca/special/mathproblems/

Word Problems for Kids from St. Francis Xavier University in Canada is designed to help students in grades 5 to 12 improve their problem solving skills. The problems are organized by grade levels, and each problem includes a hint and an answer.

Worksheet Generator

http://www.caverns.com/~mkt/Mathematics/
worksheetGenerator.html

Michael Thompson's **Worksheet Generator** creates online printable math worksheets for grades 4-12. Each worksheet can have up to 50 problems with a variety of whole number, integer, equation, greatest common factor, least common multiple, or algebra problems. Each worksheet includes a heading, a page layout, and an accompanying answer key.

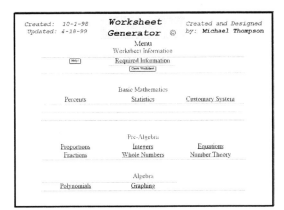

Zini's Activity Pages

http://www.incwell.com/Zini/

Zini's Activity Pages provides a collection of 40 printable, fun math activity pages for early childhood education.

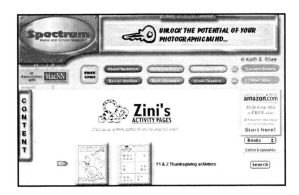

Multicultural

About.com Culture

http://home.about.com/culture/cultureamer/

About.com Culture is created by a qualified About.com Guide, a subject specialist in multiculturalism who's responsible for helping you get the most out of your time online. It contains netlinks, articles, forums, a chat room, a multiculturalism newsletter and a search engine.

Awesome Library: Multicultural Lesson Plans

http://www.neat-schoolhouse.org/Library/Materials_Search/Lesson_Plans/Multicultural.html

Awesome Library: Multicultural Lesson Plans offers teachers in K-12 more than 30 lesson plans with a multicultural theme.

Awesome Library: Multicultural Resources

http://www.awesomelibrary.org/Classroom/Social_Studies/Multicultural/Multicultural.html

Awesome Library: Multicultural Resources provides links to more than 60 sub-topics. The site also includes discussions, lesson plans, lists, materials, papers, periodicals, projects and purchase resources.

Hall of Multiculturalism

http://www.tenet.edu/academia/multi.html

Hall of Multiculturalism provides a list of multicultural resources for K-12 teachers and students. It includes links to African and African-American Resources, Asian and Asian-American Resources, Cross-Category Multicultural Resources, Indigenous People Resources, Latino/Chicano/Hispano/Mexican Resources, and Native American Resources.

Intercultural E-Mail Classroom Connections

http://www.stolaf.edu/network/iecc/

Intercultural E-Mail Classroom Connections includes mailing lists provided by St. Olaf College as a free service to help teachers and classes link with partners in other countries and cultures for e-mail, classroom, penpal, and project exchanges.

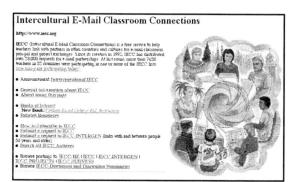

Making Multicultural Connections Through Trade Books Lesson Index

http://www.mcps.k12.md.us/curriculum/socialstd/MBD/Lessons_index.html

Making Multicultural Connections Through Trade Books Lesson Index, from the Montgomery (Maryland) County Public Schools, features multicultural trade books for elementary school students. In some instances specific lessons are included to illustrate how the trade book can be used as a classroom activity. Bibliographical information and a very brief synopsis are also provided for each book.

Multicultural Calendar

http://www.kidlink.org/KIDPROJ/MCC/

Multicultural Calendar, part of the KIDLINK Project, allows students to browse by month, author, country, or holiday. The entries contain recipes for holiday foods, historical background, significance of the holidays, and the special ways in which these days are observed.

Multicultural Pavilion

http://curry.edschool.Virginia.EDU:80/go/
multicultural/home.html

Multicultural Pavilion, sponsored by the University of Virginia and created by Paul Gorski, provides materials for teachers interested in multicultural issues. Click Teacher's Corner to find resources for K–12 teachers, including reviews of children's music, multicultural activities, online archives, and links to multicultural Web sites.

Valuing Our Differences: A Diversity Calendar

http://www3.kumc.edu/diversity/

Valuing Our Differences: A Diversity Calendar, produced by the University of Kansas for grades K–12, features ethnic, national, religious, and other types of holidays.

Multiple Subjects

A to Z Teacher Stuff: LessonPlanZ.com

http://lessonplanz.com/

LessonPlanZ.com is a searchable database of thousands of lesson plans for grades K—12. Teachers can search for individual plans or browse the subject area categories.

Academy Curriculum Exchange

http://ofcn.org/cyber.serv/academy/ace/

The **Academy Curriculum Exchange** offers hundreds of K-12 mini-lesson plans for math, science, social studies, language arts, and other subjects.

Apple Learning Exchange Lesson Plans Library

http://henson.austin.apple.com/edres/lessonmenu.shtml

Apple Learning Exchange provides a collection of technology lesson plans written by teachers and organized grade level and topics for grades K-12. Topics include art, cross curricular, language arts, mathematics, science, social studies and general.

AskERIC Lesson Plans

http://ericir.syr.edu/Virtual/Lessons/

The **AskERIC** collection contains more than 1,000 lesson plans contributed by teachers from all over the United States. They cover all grade levels and subject areas.

Ask Jeeves

http://ask.com/

Ask Jeeves a question in plain English and this Internet butler will retrieve the information you've requested instantly. For example, type "Where can I find K-12 lesson plans?" and he'll find answers for you using popular search engines. Also, click on Ask Jeeves for Kids to find hundreds of lesson plans in the teachers section.

Awesome Library: Lesson Plans

http://www.awesomelibrary.org/Library/Materials_Search/Lesson_Plans/Lesson_Plans.html

Awesome Library organizes your exploration of the World Wide Web with 10,000 carefully reviewed resources for all K–12 curriculum areas, including a lesson plan directory.

Baltimore Curriculum Project Lesson Plans

http://www.cstone.net/~bcp/BCPIntro2.htm

Baltimore Curriculum Project Lesson Plans, based on the Core Knowledge Sequence, features monthly K–5 lesson plans for variety of curricular areas. The lesson plans, organized by grade level and subject, are presented in a table.

Bigchalk.com

http://www.bigchalk.com

Bigchalk.com offers an extensive collection of lesson plans that K-12 teachers can search by keyword or browse the different subject areas. To find this searchable database, click on teachers.

Blue Web'n Learning Applications

http://www.kn.pacbell.com/wired/bluewebn/

Blue Web'n Learning Applications, provided by Pacific Bell, includes lessons, activities, projects, resources, references, and tools for the K-12 teacher. Scroll to Content Table to find more than 150 lesson plans for a various subject areas.

CEC Lesson Plans

http://www.col-ed.org/cur/

CEC Lesson Plans, sponsored by the Columbia Education Center in Portland, Oregon, features a wide variety of lesson plans created by teachers for use in their own classrooms.

Educational Units and Lesson Plans

http://coollessons.org/

Richard Levine, a teacher in the Tefft Middle School in Streamwood, Illinois, provides a treasure chest of lesson plans, units, and WebQuests for K-12 teachers.

DiscoverySchool.com: Lesson Plans Library

http://school.discovery.com/lessonplans/

DiscoverySchool.com provides hundreds of original lesson plans, all written by teachers for K-12 teachers. Use the pull down menus to browse by subject or grade level.

edHelper.com

http://edHelper.com/

This site includes more than 15,000 resources offering 7,409 lesson plans, 1,078 WebQuests, and 54 worksheet generators with a math worksheet section.

edUniverse Lesson Plans

http://eduniverse.com/lessonp.asp

This collection of 2000+ lesson plans is the result of the 1998-2000 Intel Applying Computers in Education (ACE) Project. The project trains teachers to integrate the use of computers into their own curriculum, and teachers create and submit a lesson plan as part of their final project activities. To find the entire collection K-12 lesson plans, click on Search Lesson Plans.

Education World: Lesson Planning Center

http://www.education-world.com/a_lesson/

Education World: Lesson Planning Center, sponsored by American Fidelity for grades K-12, provides weekly an article focusing on a specific topical theme such as hurricanes, first day of school, whales, or a specific holiday. In each article, teachers will find cross-curriculum lessons and activities related to the arts, history, language arts, math, science, social studies, and other topics. Each article offers printable student worksheets and links to relevant sites. In addition, scroll to Lesson Planning Resources in the Section Guide and click on it, to find hundreds of other lesson plan sources.

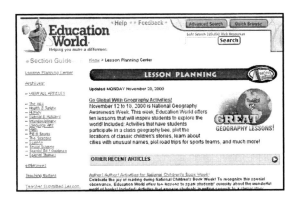

Encarta Lesson Collection

http://encarta.msn.com/schoolhouse/

Encarta Lesson Collection offers a collection of hundreds of lesson plans contributed by K–12 teachers in a wide variety of subject areas.

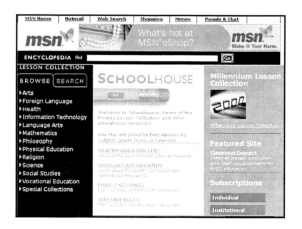

Gateway to Educational Materials

http://thegateway.org/

The **Gateway** provides a way to search for thousands of Internet lesson plans, curriculum units and other education resources. It is sponsored by The U.S. Department of Education's National Library of Education.

Gryphon House

http://www.ghbooks.com/

Gryphon House, a leading publisher of children's activity books for ages 2–7, provides hundreds of cross-curricular activities taken directly from more than 40 of the company's books. Click Free Activities to find all this material.

Helping Your Child Series

http://www.ed.gov/pubs/parents/hyc.html

U.S. Department of Education provides the **Helping Your Child Series** containing more than 150 fun activities for grades K–8. Included are writing, geography, history, math, and science activities. Selected titles are written in Spanish.

Hot Links By Subject

http://www.mcrel.org/resources/links/hotlinks.asp

McREL's **Hot Links By Subject** includes lessons and activities for the arts, language arts, mathematics, science, social studies, technology and other areas for grades K–12.

Houghton Mifflin Activity Search

http://www.eduplace.com/search/activity2.html

Houghton Mifflin features an Activity Search database for finding K–8 lesson plans in language arts, math, social studies, science, and art. Activities can also be browsed by theme.

Idea Box

http://theideabox.com/

The **Idea Box** offers hundreds of activities for early childhood teachers—mainly for preschool and kindergarten.

Index to Internet Lesson Plan Sites for K-12 Educators

http://falcon.jmu.edu/~ramseyil/lesson.htm

The Internet School Library Media Center at James Madison University provides an immense collection of lesson plan sites collected by Inez Ramsey and indexed by major subject areas. The list also includes general (multi-subject) lesson plan sites.

LessonPlansPage.com

http://www.lessonplanspage.com/

EdScope provides a searchable database of hundreds of lesson plans contributed by teachers for grades K–12.

Lesson Plan Search

http://lessonplansearch.com/

Lesson Plan Search is a searchable database of more than 2,000 lesson plans for grades K–12.

Library in the Sky: Lesson Plans

http://www.nwrel.org/sky/Library/Materials_Search/
Lesson_Plans/Lesson_Plans.html

Library in the Sky, provided by The Northwest Regional Educational Laboratory, offers hundreds of lesson plans for the major K-12 curriculum areas. The site includes a search engine and a What's New section.

Lightspan.com: Lesson Plans

http://lightspan.com/teacher/pages/tools/
default.asp?_prod=LS&_nav=t2_tools

Lightspan.com provides a searchable collection of traditional and collaborative lesson plans organized by subject for preK-12. The site also offers printable worksheets for K-8 math and language arts instruction.

New York Times Daily Lesson Plan

http://www.nytimes.com/learning/teachers/lessons/
archive.html

The *New York Times* offers an archive of hundreds of free lesson plans for grades 6-12. Each lesson plan includes a copy of a *New York Times*' article, suggested activities, and related links.

PBS TeacherSource

http://www.pbs.org/teachersource/

PBS TeacherSource features an inventory of more than 1,400 free lesson plans and online activities for grades 4-12. Many of these plans can be used independently of the TV programs.

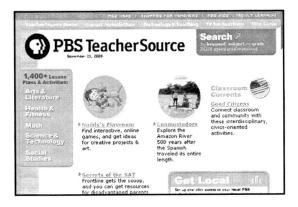

Project Center

http://www.eduplace.com/projects/

Project Center, from Houghton Mifflin, features a variety of Internet-based cooperative projects in reading, math, social studies, science, and other areas for K-12 classrooms. Teachers can also post their own projects by e-mail, and new projects are added weekly.

ProTeacher

http://www.proteacher.com/020002.shtml

ProTeacher, a resource for K-12 teachers, provides a collection of lesson plan sites for language arts, science, social studies, math, and physical education. The site also includes online activities and lessons for language arts, math, and science.

Quia Directory

http://www.quia.com/dir/

Quintessential Instructional Archive is a collection of thousands of activities categorized into 40 subject areas to complement your K-12 classroom instruction. The activities include foreign languages and vocabulary quizzes as well as alphabet, counting, math, history, and science games.

Ron MacKinnon's Educational Bookmarks

http://juliet.stfx.ca/people/stu/x94emj/
bookmark.html

Ron MacKinnon's Educational Bookmarks provides a vast collection of sites for K–12 lesson plans in math, science, social studies, foreign languages, and other curriculum areas.

Scholastic Lesson Plans & Reproducibles

http://teacher.scholastic.com/lessonrepro/

Scholastic provides a collection of teacher-tested lesson plans, ready-to-use reproducible activities, and recommended Web sites for different subject areas in grades 1-8. Each worksheet has an answer key and the worksheet can be used with any instructional program.

Science: Classroom Activities and Reproducibles

http://teacher.scholastic.com/lessonrepro/

Scholastic provides a collection of teacher-tested lesson plans, ready-to-use reproducible activities, and recommended Web sites for different subject areas in grades 1-8. The worksheets can be used independently of the Scholastic materials and have answer keys.

Sites For Teachers

http://www.sitesforteachers.com/

This teacher-friendly site contains hundreds of lesson plans, printable worksheets, and other classroom resources for grades K-12. Be sure to visit the LearningPage.com and the Sharps.

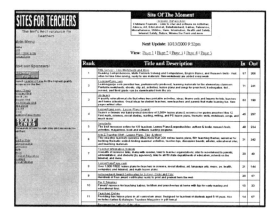

Stephanie's Lesson Plans

http://www.ibiblio.org/sashley/lesson.htm

Stephanie's Lesson Plans is a list of K-12 lesson plans for language arts, social studies, science, math, computer skills, art, and miscellaneous areas.

Study Web Teaching Resources

http://www.studyweb.com/
Professional_Development/tocteach.htm

Study Web provides hundreds of preK-12 lesson plans and printable worksheets for a wide variety of subject areas. To find these teaching resources, scroll to the middle of the page.

TeachersFirst Web Content Matrix

http://www.teachersfirst.com/matrix-f.htm

TeachersFirst Web Content Matrix, provided by the Network for Instructional Television (NITV), offers a collection of hundreds of lesson plans at the elementary, middle, and high school level. To find plans for a variety of subjects, click on lesson plans for the desired subject in the table.

Teachers.Net Lesson Bank

http://teachers.net/lessons/

The **Teachers.Net Lesson Bank,** a curriculum exchange forum for grades preK-12, provides a searchable collection of more than 400 lesson plans and activities contributed by teachers.

Teachnet.com: Lesson Ideas

http://teachnet.com/lesson/

Teachnet.com designed by teachers for K-12 teachers, offers lesson ideas for many subjects including language arts, math, science, social studies, and miscellaneous areas.

Teachers Helping Teachers

http://pacificnet.net/~mandel/#anchor581196

Teachers Helping Teachers is a source for lesson plans and suggestions contributed by teachers. The site includes plans for classroom management, language arts, science, social studies, the arts, and special education.

Teachervision.com's Lesson Plan Finder

http://www.teachervision.com/tv/curriculum/lessonplans/

Teachervision.com provides an extensive collection of lesson plans for PreK -12.

Music

Kennedy Center's ArtsEdge Arts Teaching Materials

http://artsedge.kennedy-center.org/ teaching_materials/curricula/artsedge.html

The Kennedy Center's teaching materials contains online curriculum units, lessons and activities for a variety of curriculum areas, including the performing arts.

AskERIC Lesson Plans: Music

http://ericir.syr.edu/Virtual/Lessons/Arts/Music/

AskERIC Lesson Plans: Music provides a collection of a short list of music lesson plans contributed by teachers for Grades K-12.

Elementary General Music Teaching and Learning Center

http://generalmusic.org/lessons/

This site offers interdisciplinary lessons combining music with storytelling and dance. Lessons include "Dancing with a Calypso Feel," "Themes & Tone Colors," and "Major & Pentatonic Scales."

Encarta Lesson Collection

http://www.encarta.msn.com/schoolhouse/lessons/

Encarta Lesson Collection offers a collection of lesson plans contributed by K-12 teachers in various subject areas. To find music education plans, select Arts and then click Music.

Fine Arts K to 7

http://www.bced.gov.bc.ca/irp/fak7/fak7toc.htm

Fine Arts K to 7, provided by British Columbia's Ministry of Education, includes an integrated package of lesson plans for teaching music in Grades K-7. Scroll to the Music K to 7 Curriculum, to find the plans.

GEM: Arts-Music PreK to 12

http://www.thegateway.org/index2/artsmusic.html

The **Gateway to Educational Materials (GEM),** sponsored by the U.S. Department of Education, provides a collection of art and music lesson plans and instructional resources for grades K-12.

LessonPlansPage.com

http://www.lessonplanspage.com

LessonPlansPage.com, by Kyle Yamnitz, contains a collection of music lesson plans for grades K-6.

Music Education Launch Site

http://www.talentz.com/

Music Education Launch Site, created by Jeff Brenan for grades K-12, provides a collection of music education lesson plans organized by school level and topic.

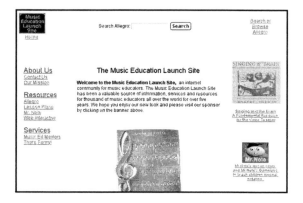

Music 8 to 10

http://www.bced.gov.bc.ca/irp/music810/mutoc.htm

Music 8 to 10, provided by British Columbia's Ministry of Education, features an integrated package of lesson plans for teaching music in grades 8, 9, and 10.

Music Teacher Resources

http://home.earthlink.net/~bluesman1/teacher.html

Music Teacher Resources contains a variety of lesson plans for grades 4-12, including African and Native American plans.

Arthur's Holiday Music Box

http://www.pbs.org/wgbh/arthur/arthur/musicbox/dswmedia/music.html

Arthur's Holiday Music Box is filled with fun holiday tunes and puzzles for preschool children. You'll need the free plug-in called Shockwave to play.

The Blue Flame Cafe

http://www.blueflamecafe.com/

The Blue Flame Cafe contains an interactive biographical encyclopedia of the great blues singers from Muddy Waters to Stevie Ray Vaughan with photos and music clips. The site is suitable for grades 7-12.

Children's Music Web Guide

http://cmw.cowboy.net/WebG/

The Children's Music Web Guide, created by Monty Harper, contains a searchable and browsable database of hundreds of children's music sites for grades K-12. Categories include Elementary Education, Fun, Live Music, Media, Music Education, Musicians/Bands, Resources, and songs.

Classical Composers' Archive

http://spight.physics.unlv.edu/

Classical Composers' Archive contains a picture gallery of composers, along with biographical information, for grades 7-12. Each day a new picture of a composer is featured on his or her birthday.

Classical MIDI Archives

http://www.prs.net/midi.html

The **Classical MIDI Archives**, arranged in an alphabetical order, offers thousands of classical music clips you can listen to at the click of the mouse. Select the Classical MIDI Archives banner and then click the desired composer's initial files. Most composers are represented. You can also use the Control Panel's keyword search engine to find a piece of classical music. The site, suitable for grades 7-12, also offers a chronology of selected composers in a timeline as well as biographies on more than 125 composers.

Classical Music

http://www.serve.com/Reid/legit.htm

Classical Music, a well-organized resource for students in grades 5-12, is a good starting point for information on classical music. The site, arranged by periods includes a chart which lists the dates, composers and timelines in which they wrote as well as sound clips of famous pieces of music for your listening pleasure.

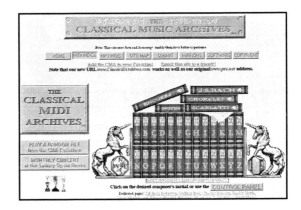

Classical Music Pages

http://w3.rz-berlin.mpg.de/cmp/classmus.html

The **Classical Music Pages**, created by Matt Boynick, provides a searchable database of almost everything you need concerning classical music. The site includes history, biographical information about composers (with portraits and short sound examples), explanations of the various musical forms, and a dictionary of musical terminologies. It is designed to be of use for everyone from "beginners" to the music professional.

Classical Music Resources

http://www.lib.duke.edu/music/resources/
classical_index.html

This site provides a comprehensive collection of classical music resources on the Web. You'll find links to nearly 2,000 non-commercial sites in more than a dozen languages.

ClassicalNet Home Page

http://www.classical.net/

ClassicalNet Home Page, for grades 5–12, provides a wide array of resources about classical music. The site includes a list of recommended CDs, biographical data about famous composers, and more than 2,500 related links.

Educational Standards and Curriculum Frameworks for Art and Music

http://PutnamValleySchools.org/StSu/Art.html

Educational Standards and Curriculum Frameworks for Art and Music is an annotated list of Internet sites with K–12 educational standards and curriculum frameworks documents, maintained by Charles Hill and the Putnam Valley Schools in New York.

Fun Music Ideas

http://www.funmusicideas.com/

Fun Music Ideas is a free monthly e-mail newsletter that is electronically mailed to subscribers once a month. It is jammed packed with helpful ideas, songs, games, teaching techniques, and is a virtual tool kit for anyone involved in teaching music. To view past issues online dating back to 1997, click on archives.

Index Of Rounds

http://www-personal.umich.edu/~msmiller/
rounds.html

Index Of Rounds contains a collection of rounds, including images of the music, lyrics, and sound clips for grades 4–12.

Internet Music Resource Guide

http://www.teleport.com/~celinec/music.shtml

Internet Music Resource Guide features links to a variety of music resources, including bands and artists, magazines, and search sites. For an extensive list of everything musical on the Web, click General Sites.

Instrument Encyclopedia

http://www.si.umich.edu/CHICO/MHN/
enclpdia.html

The Music Heritage Network offers the history (and photographs) of musical instruments. You can search for your instrument by geographic area, orchestra section or by the name of the instrument itself.

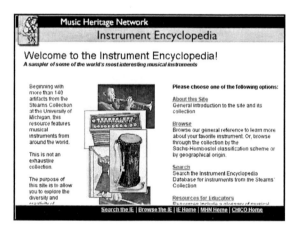

Jazz Online

http://www.jazzonln.com/

Jazz Online contains reviews, artist bios, music and video clips, events and club listings, radio links, and more.

John Phillip Sousa Page

http://www.dws.org/sousa/

John Phillip Sousa Page contains hundreds of sound clips of band music you can listen to on your computer written by this great American composer. The site, suitable for grades 3-12, also includes related links, photos, and historical information on the "March King's" life.

Judy and David Page

http://judyanddavid.com/

The **Judy and David Page** is the site for the Canadian music show for preschool and elementary school kids. Teachers will find a catalog of children's music, which includes the lyrics to many popular children's songs. Photos from the show, sound clips of some of the show's music, and links to other children's sites are also featured.

K-12 Resources for Music Educators

http://www.isd77.k12.mn.us/resources/staffpages/shirk/k12.music.html

K-12 Resources for Music Educators contains important resources for music teachers and students in all areas of the music curriculum.

Land of Music

http://www.landofmusic.com/

The **Land of Music** provides songs and activities to teach the theory concept in the primary grades. It's the home of the Note Family, the Rest Family, and many more characters, making notes, other musical symbols and instruments come alive for the kids. Everyone in the Land of Music helps to build Songhouses (songs) of all styles. They teach how to read, write and enjoy music through songs, stories, games, movement, puzzles and books.

Mama Lisa's World

http://www.mamalisa.com/world/

Mama Lisa's World contains a collection of children's songs and nursery rhymes from all over the globe, in English and their native languages. The site is suitable for grades K-6.

Mark Corey's Music Stuff!

http://www.mcs.net/~mcorey/mustuf.htm

Mark Corey's Music Stuff! contains a collection of Web sites for band, orchestra, and choir directors, as well as musicians and music educators. The site is suitable for grades K-12.

MIDIs for Kiddies

http://www.concentric.net/~Gamba/

MIDIs for Kiddies contains a collection of children's music written by D.F. Saphra for grades 4-8. Categories include African-American history songs, seasonal songs, and health and safety songs. You can listen to the music on your computer as well as print many of the lyrics for use in the classroom.

MoJo's Musical Mouseum

http://www.kididdles.com/mouseum/

MoJo's Musical Mouseum, created by KIDiddles for grades K-5, contains a collection over the 250 lyrics to children's songs organized alphabetically and by subject. You can also use a keyword search engine to find a song as well as request that your favorite song be listed on the site.

Music Education for Young Children

http://www.2-life.com/meyc/

Music Education for Young Children, maintained by Deborah Pratt, features teaching ideas, songs and music games, music curricula, and other resources for grades PreK-12.

Music Education Online

http://www.geocities.com/Athens/2405/

Music Education Online, maintained by Larry Newman, features an interactive message board and chat room, hundreds of links, news articles, and book reviews for grades K-12.

Music Education Resources

http://www.bright.net/~lruggles/musiced.html

Music Education Resources catalogs hundreds of links dealing with Music Theory, Music Software, Lyrics, Music History , Resources, Professional Organizations, FTP Sites, Music Clip Art, and Instrumental Sites for grades K-12.

Music Games Page

http://home.earthlink.net/~bluesman1/games.html

The **Music Games Page** provides ideas and classroom activities for making learning music fun in grades 4-8. For additional ideas, be sure to click on What's New? More Games!

Music History 102: A Guide to Western Composers and Their Music

http://www.ipl.org/exhibit/mushist/

Internet Public Library's **Music History 102** is a survey of western classical music from the middle ages to the twentieth century for high school students. The guide includes information on more than 30 composers, music clips and images of each historical period.

Music Lyrics

http://home.earthlink.net/~jmak/Music/Lyrics.html

Music Lyrics, collected by Sue Wichers for grades K-12, is list of links to many lyrics sites, including folk, international, scouts, kids, by artists, and others. Some of the sites include sound clips.

Music Notes Interactive

http://library.thinkquest.org/15413/

Music Notes Interactive lets you explore online various styles of music from Bach to rock. The site provides information on note reading, intervals, scales, chords, and other useful music education topics for grades 7-12.

Music Teacher's Resource Site

http://www.mtrs.co.uk

The **Music Teacher's Resource Site** includes an Ask-an-expert page where you can find online help from a list of music education experts, equipment & instrument reviews, arrangements and class projects, vocal and instrumental rounds, as well as lyrics you can print out and songs with MIDI file you can enjoy listening to on your computer.

National School Network Exchange: Music Online

http://nsn.bbn.com/motet/

The **National School Network Exchange: Music Online** provides a variety of curriculum materials for grades 9-12. They range from understanding melody and themes to spotting the historical and cultural context of music and include sound files. Scroll to MOTET Curriculum to find the materials.

OperaGlass

http://rick.stanford.edu/opera/main.html

OperaGlass provides a variety of opera resources for grades 9-12. The site includes 100 well-known and lesser-known opera composers, with complete opera lists and links to pages containing information on about 250 operas with synopses, libretti, performance histories, discographies, and essays.

Phil's Famous Movie and TV Music Themes

http://freespace.virgin.net/philip.churchyard/pc4.html

Phil's Famous Movie and TV Music Themes is a collection of sound clips from scores of popular movie and TV shows you can listen to on your computer. The site is suitable for grades K-12.

Piano Education Page

http://www.unm.edu/~loritaf/pnoedmn.html

The **Piano Education Page**, in English and Spanish, contains tips on learning to play the piano, a competition calendar, finding the right piano teacher, getting information on music software, more than 600 music-related sites, and other music education resources for grades K-12. The site also includes an audition room that offers 500 piano music and sound clips for your listening pleasure with links to composer biographies. Children can visit Just for Kids to play games and meet composers.

Pure Illusion MIDI Collection

http://www.facethemusic.org/midisite/

Pure Illusion MIDI Collection contains an eclectic collection of music that students in grades 6-12 can enjoy listening to on the computer. The site includes fun classical, rock 'n' roll, TV themes, the movies, Disney, kids, oldies, soul, and Motown.

Robert's MIDI Jukebox

http://meltingpot.fortunecity.com/kentish/116/midi/

Robert's MIDI Jukebox features a list of more than 300 sound clips from the movies, TV programs, and pop songs for your listening pleasure. The site is suitable for grades 4-12.

Schoolhouse Rock

http://genxtvland.simplenet.com/
SchoolHouseRock/index-lo.shtml

Schoolhouse Rock lets you take a trip back to the 1970s. The site contains more than 40 original Schoolhouse Rock songs for different subject areas to share with students in grades 3-6.

Scouter's Belay: Songbook

http://cac.psu.edu/~jxm181/songs.html

This site offers an alphabetical list of more than 100 printable songs for elementary school children.

This Day In Music History

http://DataDragon.com/day/

This Day In Music History presents daily the birthdays of well-known composers and songwriters, the openings of Broadway shows and plays, and links to songs that made the charts. The site is suitable for grades 7-12.

Yahoo!: Classical Music Shopping

http://shopping.yahoo.com/musicshopping/
bygenre/classical/

Yahoo!: Classical Composers introduces students in grades 5-12 to hundreds of composers from baroque to twentieth century periods. Select a musical period and click a composer's name to find biographical information, pictures, and descriptions of the composer's work.

Yahoo!: Genres

http://dir.yahoo.com/Entertainment/Music/Genres/

Yahoo!: Genres contains a collection of hundreds of sites to every kind of musical style, including children's, classical, folk, jazz, and rock and pop for grades K-12.

Science

Academy Curriculum Exchange

http://ofcn.org/cyber.serv/academy/ace/

The **Academy Curriculum Exchange** offers lesson plans for grades K-12 in a variety of subject areas. To find more than 200 plans for science, click Elementary School, Intermediate School, or High School.

Access Excellence
Activities Exchange

http://www.accessexcellence.org/AE/

Access Excellence Activities Exchange, sponsored by Genentech, contains an archive of hundreds of lessons and activities submitted by high school biology and life science teachers participating in the Access Excellence Program.

ACCESS INDIANA Teaching
& Learning Center

http://tlc.ai.org/

The **ACCESS INDIANA Teaching & Learning Center** provides a collection of science lesson plans for grades K-12. To find them, click on Teacher Lesson Plans in the Science section.

Activity Search

http://www.eduplace.com/search/activity2.html

Activity Search, from Houghton Mifflin, features a curriculum database where K-8 teachers can search for science lesson plans/activities and other subject areas by grade level. Activities can also be browsed by theme.

Africanized Honey Bees
on the Move Lesson Plans

http://ag.arizona.edu/pubs/insects/ahb/

Africanized Honey Bees on the Move Lesson Plans, maintained by Roberta Gibson at the University of Arizona, features 30 lesson plans for grades K-12 organized by grade clusters. The plans are also integrated with information and activity sheets.

Air Quality Lesson Plans and Data

http://www.tnrcc.state.tx.us/air/monops/lessons/lesson_plans.html

Air Quality Lesson Plans and Data, provided by the Texas Natural Resource Conservation Commission, features lesson plans and activities to teach the subject of air quality in the K-12 classroom.

ALCOMed

http://olbers.kent.edu/alcomed/Sam_Net/samnet.html

Advanced Liquid Crystalline Optical Materials (ALCOM) Education Outreach Program provides a collection of K-12 lesson plans prepared by a team of teachers participating in two workshops at Kent State University. Links to the plans can be found at the bottom of the page. Also, the Ask a Scientist section at the top offers lesson ideas.

Amazing Science at the Roxy

http://www.hood-consulting.com/amazing/qt_amazing/asr.html

Amazing Science at the Roxy, provided by Hood Consulting Group, features physical science lesson plans and experiments for grades 5-12.

Amazing Space

http://amazing-space.stsci.edu/

The Space Telescope Science Institute, responsible for the scientific operation of the Hubble Space Telescope, provides a variety of interactive Web-based space lessons and activities for grades 6-12. All lessons include spectacular photographs taken by the Hubble Space Telescope. Activities offered are Galaxies Galore, Star Light, Star Bright, Solar System Trading Cards, Hubble Deep Field Academy, Astronaut Challenge, and Galileo to the Hubble Space Telescope.

AskERIC Lesson Plans

http://ericir.syr.edu/Virtual/Lessons/Science/

AskERIC Lesson Plans provides a collection of science lesson plans contributed by teachers for grades K-12. Topics include agriculture, biological and life sciences, earth science, physical sciences, space sciences, and technology. Each lesson plan features an overview, purpose, objectives, activities, and resource materials.

Astronomy with a Stick

http://www.nsta.org/programs/sst/aws/

Astronomy with a Stick, sponsored by the National Science Teachers Association, contains daytime astronomy units for upper elementary and middle school students around the world. Registered classes can also share data, stories, and questions about astronomy with each other.

Athena

http://www.athena.ivv.nasa.gov/

Athena, sponsored by NASA for grades K-12, features online science lessons and activities. Topics include oceans, earth, weather, atmosphere, space, and astronomy.

Awesome Library:
Science Lesson Plans

http://www.awesomelibrary.org/Library/
Materials_Search/Lesson_Plans/Science.html

The **Awesome Library** contains a collection of hundreds of science lesson plans for grades K-12.

Bigchalk.com: Teachers

http://www.bigchalk.com/

Bigchalk.com provides a vast searchable collection of science lesson plans arranged by grade level and topic. Click on Teachers and browse the lesson plan archives to find earth, life, and physical science lessons for grades K-12.

Biology Lessons for Teachers

http://public.sdsu.edu/NaturalSciences/

Biology Lessons for Teachers, contributed by students at San Diego State University, features biology lesson plans for elementary classrooms. Lessons part 1 covers molecules and cells, and Lessons part 2 covers population biology.

CEC Lesson Plans

http://www.col-ed.org/cur/#Sci

CEC Lesson Plans, sponsored by the Columbia Education Center in Portland, Oregon, features a wide variety of lesson plans created by teachers for use in classrooms. There are science plans for elementary (K-5), intermediate (6-8), and high school (9-12).

CIPCO's Teacher's Lounge

http://cipco.electricuniverse.com/html/eu/education/
teacher/

The Central Iowa Power Cooperative (**CIPCO**), headquartered in Cedar Rapids, provides lesson plans and experiments covering chemistry, electricity, and energy for grades K-6.

Cody's Science Education Zone

http://ousdmail.ousd.k12.ca.us/~codypren/lessons.html

Cody's Science Education Zone provides a variety of lesson plans prepared by Anthony Cody, a middle school science teacher in Oakland, California.

Connections+

http://www.mcrel.org/resources/plus/science

Connections+, provided by Mid-Continent Regional Educational Laboratory (McREL), contains of science lesson plans, activities, and curriculum resources categorized by topic for grades K-12.

Connecting Students

http://www.connectingstudents.com/

Connecting Students, maintained by David Leahy, provides a collection of Internet-ready lesson plans for grades K-12. Teachers will find language arts plans in the lesson plans, themes, Web lessons, and literacy sections.

CNF Beetle Survey

http://www.schoolnet.ca/vp-pv/ladybug/e/ladybuge/

Canadian Nature Federation (CNF) Lady Beetle Survey provides lesson plans (Teacher's Kit), printable student activity sheets, background information, and pictures of different lady beetles. The material is appropriate for students in grades 4–8.

Dow/NSTA Summer Workshop

http://thechalkboard.com/NSTA.html

The **Dow/NSTA Summer Workshop** provides a collection of chemistry lessons and activities developed by teachers participating in 1995, 1996, and 1997 workshops. This material is suitable for high school students.

Educate the Children: Lesson Plans

http://www.educate.org.uk/teacher_zone/classroom/science/index.htm

Educate the Children provides a collection of more than 65 lesson plans and hundreds of worksheets contributed by teachers for grades K-12.

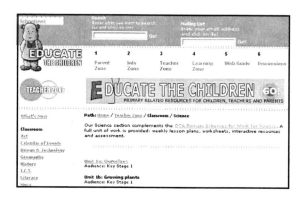

Education World: Science Lesson Plans

http://db.education-world.com/perl/browse?cat_id=1878

Education World, sponsored by American Fidelity Services, provides nearly 225 science lesson plans for grades K-12. Categories include Agriculture, Life Science, Natural History, Physical Science, Space, and Technology. For additional lesson plans submitted by teachers, click on Teacher Lessons and go to science in the left panel.

EE Link: Classroom Resources— Directories

http://eelink.net/classroomresources-directories.html

EE Link provides a searchable collection of environmental education sites organized by topic. Many of the sites offer lesson plans and activities for K-12. Topics include fresh water, oceans and coasts, air and climate, endangered species, toxics and waste management, wildlife and biodiversity, and endangered species.

ENC: Lessons and Activities-Science

http://www.enc.org/professional/timesavers/
lessonplans/science/

The Eisenhower Clearinghouse for Mathematics and Science Education (**ENC**) provides a collection of sites with science lesson plans and activities for grades K-12.

Encarta Lesson Collection

http://www.encarta.msn.com/schoolhouse/menus/
menuscience.asp

Encarta Lesson Collection offers a collection of science lesson plans contributed by K-12 teachers. Topics range from general science to astronomy and physics.

Endangered Species in Endangered Spaces

http://rbcm1.rbcm.gov.bc.ca/end_species/
es_plans/es_plans.html

Endangered Species in Endangered Spaces offers more than 25 lesson plans prepared by Carol Thomson of Okanagan College in British Columbia. Although these lessons were designed for Canadian students, they will fit into any environmental education curriculum for grades 2-7.

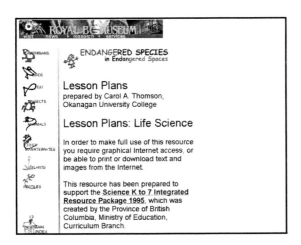

Educational Resources in Science

http://www.cln.org/subjects/science.html

The British Columbia Community Learning Network provides lesson plans, worksheets, theme pages, and curricular resources teaching science in grades K-12.

Engaging Science Lesson Plan Exchange

http://www.engagingscience.org/lpe/lpe.htm

Engaging Science contains a searchable collection of science lesson plans created by British Columbia teachers for grades K-7. Teachers everywhere are encouraged to submit their own lessons.

EnviroLink Network

http://envirolink.netforchange.com/

EnviroLink Network provides a searchable collection of lesson plans and activities for teaching environmental education in grades K-12. To find this material, click on educational resources in the left panel.

Explore Our Resources

http://www.sln.org/resources/

Explore Our Resources contains a wide variety of science lessons and activities from museums in the Science Learning Network for grades K-6. Among the topics are acids and bases, El Niño, science of balloons, physics of water fountains, hurricanes, wind, volcanoes, cow's eye dissection, and light, shadow, and images.

Explorer

http://explorer.scrtec.org/explorer/

Explorer offers a large collection of science lesson plans and activities for grades K-12. Click Natural Sciences Curriculum to find plans for general science, life science, physical science, earth science, and common themes. Or search for specific science lesson plans in the Explorer database.

Florida Aquarium: Hands On

http://www2.sptimes.com/aquarium/FA.4.html

The **Florida Aquarium** provides hands-on lessons and other resources for wannabe marine biologists of all ages. The site also features background information for teachers.

Frank Potter's Science Gems

http://sciencegems.com/

Frank Potter's Science Gems contains hundreds of science resources sorted by category, topic, and grade level useful for teachers and students in grades K-12. To find Internet-based, WebQuest lesson plans contributed by teachers, scroll to Special Resource Links.

From A Distance

http://education.ssc.nasa.gov/ltp/

John C. Stennis Space Center's **From A Distance** contains a collection of K-12 Internet-based, space science lesson plans developed by teachers and organized by grade level.

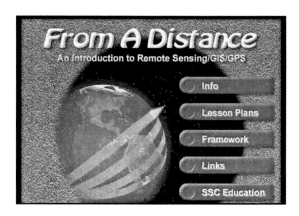

Gateway to Educational Materials

http://thegateway.org/

The **Gateway**, sponsored by the U.S. Department of Education, provides access to hundreds of lesson plans on the Internet, curriculum units, and other education resources for grades K-12. To find a list of science plans, select Browse Subject and click on Science.

GCRIO: It's Elementary

http://www.gcrio.org/edu/elementary/itselem.html

The US Global Change Research Information Office (**GCRIO**) provides a variety of environmental lesson plans for grades K-8.

Goose Holler Middle School Science Activities

http://www.serve.com/chunter/

Craig Hunter provides science lesson plan ideas for teaching middle school students.

Hands-On Science Lesson Plans

http://student.biology.arizona.edu/sciconn/lessons.html

University of Arizona Secondary Science Education students provides a collection of biology, earth science, chemistry, and physics lessons for grades 9-12.

Imagine the Universe!

http://imagine.gsfc.nasa.gov/

NASA's **Imagine the Universe** provides math and science teacher-created lesson plans and other resources about astronomy and space exploration for high school students. Click on Teachers Corner to find the plans. The site also includes Ask a NASA Scientist service, an online dictionary of astrophysics terms, and related links.

Insects in the Classroom: Bugs as teaching tools for all ages

http://entowww.tamu.edu/academic/ucourses/ento489/

Texas A&M University's **Insects in the Classroom** contains a collection of teacher-created lesson plans organized by age, grade level, and topic for grades K-12. For more teaching ideas about entomology, click on Course Activities.

John Glenn, American Hero

http://www.pbs.org/kcet/johnglenn/

John Glenn, American Hero, a companion site to the PBS program, provides a detailed look at STS-95, a collection of cross-curricular lesson plans and interactive space games and considers the future of space flight in the 21st century, including the International Space Station. The site is suitable for grades 5-12.

JPL's Links to Learning

http://eis.jpl.nasa.gov/eao/class.html

Jet Propulsion Laboratory (**JPL**) and NASA offers a wealth of earth and space science lesson plans for students and teachers in grades K–12. For more curriculum resources, click on Teachers.

K-8 Aeronautics Internet Textbook

http://wings.ucdavis.edu/

The **K-8 Aeronautics Internet Textbook**, developed by Cislunar Aerospace, provides a comprehensive study of the science of aeronautics for elementary and middle school students over the Internet. The text has various reading levels and a Spanish version. The site includes lesson plans with fun experiments and exercises to help students understand the contents of the textbook and also a variety of cross-curriculum activities. The Scientists and Engineers' Guide features a list more than 36 experiments that can be used in any K-8 science curriculum.

Langley Distributed Active Archive Center

http://eosweb.larc.nasa.gov/education/Erb_Intro.html

The NASA **Langley Distributed Active Archive Center** provides a collection of cross-curricular earth science lesson plans, experiments, and follow-up activities to help middle school students learn about atmospheric conditions. The site includes a glossary and other resources.

Lesson Index

http://www.crpc.rice.edu/CRPC/GT/dawsonm/lesindex.htm

Marcella Dawson provides a collection of earth, life science, physics lessons and Web activities she authored for students in grades 6-12.

LessonPlansPage.com

http://lessonplanspage.com/Science.htm

Kyle Yamnitz's **LessonPlansPage.com** contains a collection of science lesson plans organized by grade level for grades K–12.

Lesson Stop

http://www.youthline-usa.com/lessonstop/

Lesson Stop, maintained by Therese Sarah, contains more than 500 sites with thousands of lesson plans for grades K-12. The site includes science plans organized by topic and grade level.

Library in the Sky

http://www.nwrel.org/sky/Library/Materials_search/
Lesson_Plans/Science.html

The **Library in the Sky** by Northwest Regional Educational Laboratory (NWREL) contains a collection of science lesson plans for grades K-12.

Lightspan.com: Lesson Plans

http://lightspan.com/teacher/pages/tools/
default.asp?_prod=LS&_nav=t2_tools

Lightspan.com provides an extensive collection of traditional and collaborative lesson plans for preK-12. To find science plans, click Lesson Plans.

Link-to-Learn Classroom Activities

http://l2l.org/pd/tch_classroom.html

Link-to-Learn, an initiative of the Commonwealth of Pennsylvania, contains hundreds of Internet-enriched lesson plans and activities contributed by teachers for the elementary school, middle school, and high school. Math teachers can find classroom activities by title or grade level. Each classroom activity includes a plan to organize and structure the lesson, an activity worksheet that can be used online or printed for use as a handout, and extension tips with related sites for the lesson.

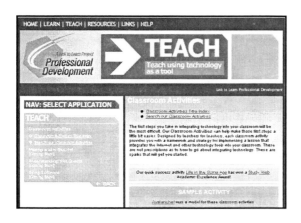

McREL: Lesson Plans and Activities

http://www.mcrel.org/resources/links/lesson.asp

McREL: Lesson Plans and Activities, gathered by Mid-Continent Regional Educational Laboratory (McREL), contains a collection of science lesson plan sites for grades K-12.

Miami Museum of Science: Online Resources

http://www.miamisci.org/www/sln.html

Miami Museum of Science provides a variety of online resources and activities for students in grades 3-8. The pH Factor introduces acids and bases, the Atoms Family contains activities about energy concepts, Hurricane: Storm Science teaches about hurricanes the inside out, and Ecolinks features environmental information, ideas, and research online.

Middle School Institute for Math-Science Integration (MSIMSI)

http://www.owu.edu/~mggrote/msi2/

MSIMSI contains integrated middle school math/science lesson plans developed by teachers in a summer workshop held at Ohio Wesleyan University.

Minnetonka Public Schools

http://www.minnetonka.k12.mn.us/science/
teacher.html

The **Minnetonka Public Schools** in Minnesota provide a collection of science lesson plans organized by grade level for the elementary school. To find more science plans, scroll and click on Project Link.

Modeling Intermediate Science Teaching (MIST)

http://www.owu.edu/~mggrote/mist/

MIST contains a collection of science lesson plans developed by Ohio Wesleyan University science professors for teachers in grades 4-6. Included are activities for botany, chemistry, geology, physics, and zoology.

NASA Glenn Learning Technologies Project

http://www.grc.nasa.gov/WWW/K-12/

NASA Glenn Learning Technologies Project provides a wide variety of aeronautic and space resources and lesson plans for students in grades 7-12.

Nebraska Earth Science Education Network

http://nesen.unl.edu/teacher/lesacttoc.html

The Nebraska Earth Science Education Network (NESEN) provides a collection of lesson plans and activities developed by teachers for K-12 classrooms. Topics range from geology to water to soils to weather. Activites are categorized by grade level and topic.

Newton's Apple

http://ericir.syr.edu/Projects/Newton/

PBS's **Newton's Apple** features a collection of more than 120 science lessons from seasons 9 through 15 for grades 3-8. The lessons cover a wide variety of science topics and can be used independently of the television program. The site also includes an alphabetical list of all of the lessons and Science Try Its (experiments) to accompany each lesson.

NSTA's Scope, Sequence & Coordination Project

http://dev.nsta.org/ssc/

The National Science Teachers Association (**NSTA**) provides a wide range of micro-units for biology, chemistry, earth/space, and physics for students in grades 9-12. To view the lessons tied to the National Science Education Standards, you must douwnload Adobe's free Acrobat Reader.

Neurolab Online (NeurOn)

http://quest.arc.nasa.gov/neuron/

The Teachers' Lounge of NASA's NeurOn provides a collection of lesson plans, experiments, and other neuroscience lesson plan sites for grades 3-12. Students can also ask the NASA experts questions and read answers.

Neuroscience Laboratories and Classroom Activities

http://lshome.utsa.edu/programs/Neurobiology/nlca/NLCA.htm

The University of Texas at San Antonio offers a dozen neuroscience lessons and activities for grades 7-12. To view and print this material, you must download Adobe's free Acrobat Reader.

Ocean Planet

http://seawifs.gsfc.nasa.gov/OCEAN_PLANET/HTML/search_educational_materials.html

Ocean Planet, for grades K-12, is a Smithsonian Institution exhibit containing a collection of lesson plans and other online resources for teaching about marine life.

Physical Science Activity Manual

http://cesme.utm.edu/resources/science/PSAM.html

The **Physical Science Activity Manual** features 34 hands-on science lesson activities for grades 8-10. Topics include the learning cycle, density, physical and chemical properties, mixtures, Newton's three Laws, and air pressure. To view the materials, you must download Adobe's free Acrobat Reader.

Physics 98 Institute Lesson Plans

http://www.owu.edu/%7emggrote/phys98/lessons.html

Physics 98 contains 20 high school physics lesson plans developed by Ohio teachers attending a 1998 summer institute held at Ohio Wesleyan University.

Project Galileo: Bringing Jupiter to Earth

http://www.jpl.nasa.gov/galileo/

Project Galileo: Bringing Jupiter to Earth provides an assortment of lessons and activities on the space probe for grades 5-12. To find these materials, click on Education at the top menu bar.

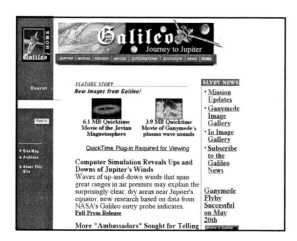

Project Primary

http://www.owu.edu/~mggrote/pp/

Project Primary provides a collection of hands-on science lesson plans developed by Ohio Wesleyan University science professors for teachers in grades K-3. Included are activities for botany, chemistry, geology, physics, and zoology.

Rainforest Workshop

http://kids.osd.wednet.edu/Marshall/rainforest_home_page.html

The **Rainforest Workshop,** for middle school students, provides a variety of lesson plans and activities about temperate and tropical rain forests. To find these plans, click Educational Resources and scroll to Lesson Plans and Activities.

Scholastic Lesson Plans & Reproducibles

http://teacher.scholastic.com/lessonrepro/

Scholastic provides a collection of teacher-tested lesson plans, ready-to-use reproducible activities, and recommended Web sites for science topics in grades 1–8. The worksheets can be used independently of Scholastic materials and have answer keys.

SciCentral: Lesson Plans

http://www.sciquestfoundation.org/k12/K-lesson.html

SciCentral provides a collection of science sites with hundreds of lesson plans for grades K-12.

Science Lessons by Subject

http://www.eecs.umich.edu/~coalitn/sciedoutreach/funexperiments/agesubject/subject.html

The Southeastern Michigan Math-Science Learning Coalition provides a collection of lessons and experiments for astronomy, biology, chemistry, earth science, and physical science. Lessons are also sorted by age group from early elementary to high school.

Science Education Gateway (SEGway)

http://cse.ssl.berkeley.edu/segway_home/

SEGway, a partnership of university scientists, NASA, and educators, provides a variety of lesson plans for the study of space science the solar system in grades 4-12. To find these plans, click on Educators. The site also includes online interactive lessons on comets, light, and spectra in the Public section.

Schoolhouse: Science

http://teacherpathfinder.org/School/science.html

Schoolhouse: Science, part of Teacher/Pathfinder, provides a collection of science lesson plans for grades K-12. Topics include anatomy, chemistry, and weather. You can also search the site for lesson plans.

SCORE Science: Lessons and Activities

http://scorescience.humboldt.k12.ca.us/fast/teachers/lessons.htm

SCORE Science, part of the Schools of California Online Resource for Educators, provides a searchable database of lesson plans and activities linked to the California content science standards for grades K-12. To find the complete list of the plans, select All grades and All Subjects and click Show Lessons.

SeaWorld/Busch Gardens Educational Resources

http://www.seaworld.org/teacherguides/teacherguides.html

SeaWorld/Busch Gardens provides over a dozen guides for teaching about animals and the environment in grades K-12. Each teacher's guide contains lesson plans and hand-on science activities. To find more science materials, scroll to the bottom of the page and click on Classroom Activities.

SETI Institute

http://www.seti-inst.edu/education/litu-bg.html

Search for Extraterrestrial Intelligence (SETI) Institute offers sample lessons from its Life in the Universe Curriculum Project for elementary and middle school students.

Severe Weather Information Kit

http://nesen.unl.edu/swik/

The Nebraska Earth Science Education Network (NESEN) provides a series of severe weather preparedness lessons, along with accompanying resources such as experiments and safety tips.

SMILE Program

The Science and Mathematics Initiative for Learning Enhancement (**SMILE**) program, maintained by the Illinois Institute of Technology, features more than 200 lesson plans in each of these major science subjects, developed by teachers for grades K-12:

✉ Biology Index

http://www.iit.edu/~smile/biolinde.html

Topics include anatomy and physiology, zoology, botany, microbiology, environmental studies and ecology, biochemistry, and general biology. Each plan includes objectives, the materials needed, suggested strategy, and expected outcomes.

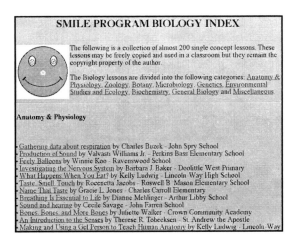

✉ Chemistry Index

http://www.iit.edu/~smile/cheminde.html

Topics include basic tools and principles, atomic and molecular structure, states of matter, chemical reactions, chemistry of elements, compounds and materials. Each plan includes objectives, the materials needed, suggested strategy, and expected outcomes.

✉ Physics Index

http://www.iit.edu/~smile/physinde.html

Topics include matter, mechanics, fluids, electricity and magnetism, waves, sound and optics, and miscellaneous. Each plan includes objectives, the materials needed, suggested strategy, and expected outcomes.

Smithsonian Education: Lesson Plans

http://educate.si.edu/resources/lessons/
lessons.html

The **Smithsonian** Office of Elementary and Secondary Education provides classroom ready lesson plans and activites integrating science with other curriculum areas in grades K- 6.

Spaceborne Imaging Radar-C Education

http://ericir.syr.edu/Projects/NASA/nasa.html

Spaceborne Imaging Radar-C Education (SIR-CED) is the latest generation of imaging radars produced by the Jet Propulsion Laboratory for NASA. This site offers a Teacher's Resource Guide and a Lesson Guide for middle school and high school students and teachers.

STELLAR Online

http://stellar.arc.nasa.gov/stellar/

The **Science Training for Enhancing Leadership and Learning Through Accomplishments in Research (STELLAR)**, sponsored by the NASA Ames Research Center, provides lesson plans and hands-on activities developed by teachers for the study of space life sciences in grades K-12.

Summer Research Program for Science Teachers

http://www.scienceteacherprogram.org/
tchrplan.html

The Columbia University **Summer Research Program** offers a collection of more than 2,000 laboratory lesson plans developed by the participating teachers for high school science.

Teacher-Developed Earth and Space Science Lessons and Classroom Activities

http://w3.cea.berkeley.edu/Education/lessons/
lessons_teacherdeveloped.html

Teacher-Developed Earth and Space Science Lessons and Classroom Activities, from the University of California, Berkeley, is a collection of science lesson plans on weather, satellites, auroras, and earthquakes aimed at grades 4-12.

Teaching N' Technology

http://twister.coedu.usf.edu/tnt/

Teaching N' Technology (TNT), is a database of more than 400 technology-related lesson plans developed by Florida teachers for grades 4-12. The site includes plans for science as well as other subject areas matched to Florida's Sunshine State Standards. Each lesson plan contains computer and subject information and provides detailed instructions on how to implement the lesson in your classroom. You can search for plans by subject area, grade level, and keyword.

Teachnet.Com

http://teachnet.com/lesson/

Teachnet.Com, designed by teachers for K-12 teachers, offers science lesson ideas for biology, earth, physics, scientific method, space and time, weather, and general areas.

TeachersFirst Web Content Matrix

http://www.teachersfirst.com/matrix-f.htm

TeachersFirst Web Content Matrix, provided by the Network for Instructional Television (NITV), offers a collection of lesson plans at the elementary, middle, and high school levels. To find science plans, scroll to a science subject in the table, and click on lesson plans.

Teachervision.com's
Lesson Plan Finder

http://www.teachervision.com/tv/curriculum/lessonplans/

Teachervision.com, part of the Learning Network, provides an extensive collection of lesson plans for PreK -12. To find science plans, use the grade level and the subject pull down menus.

TEAMS Distance Learning:
K-12 Lesson Plans

http://teams.lacoe.edu/documentation/places/lessons.html

TEAMS Distance Learning, maintained by the Los Angeles County Office of Education, provides a collection of lessons plan sites for grades K-12 organized by subject. To find science lesson plans, click Science.

Unit Plan:
The Impact of Shoemaker-Levy 9

http://www.smplanet.com/science/science.html

Small Planet Communications offers an Internet-based astronomy unit for middle school students. The unit covers the impact of the Shoemaker-Levy 9 comet on the planet Jupiter.

Using Live Insects in Elementary Classrooms for Early Lessons in Life

http://insected.arizona.edu/uli.htm

The Center for Insect Science Education at the University of Arizona provides a collection of printable 20 integrated lesson plans with science and math activities that use live insects for primary grade children. These lessons introduce health topics to children and are aligned with National Science Education Standards (NSES).

Volcano World Lesson Plans

http://volcano.und.nodak.edu/vwdocs/vwlessons/lesson.html

Volcano World offers volcano-related lessons and classroom activities for grades 4-12.

Weather Here and There

http://www.ncsa.uiuc.edu/edu/RSE/RSEred/WeatherHome.html

Weather Here and There is an interactive weather unit incorporating hands-on, collaborative problem-solving activities for students in grades 4-6.

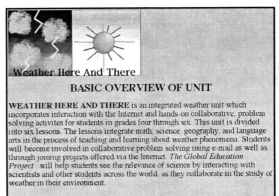

The Weather Unit

http://faldo.atmos.uiuc.edu/WEATHER/weather.html

The Weather Unit is a collection of thematic lesson plans for grades 2–4. It integrates the study of weather into all curricular areas. Click Science to find 14 science lessons, including Water Cycle, Rain Game, and Light and Heat.

WeatherEye

http://weathereye.kgan.com/

WeatherEye, maintained by Scott Hall and Roger Evans of KGAN Newschannel 2 in Cedar Rapids, Iowa, features lesson plans, experiments, and other online resources for the study of weather in grades K–12.

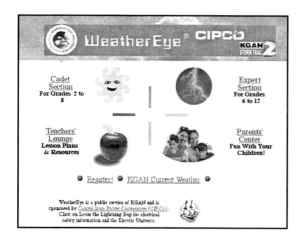

Whales: A Thematic Web Unit

http://curry.edschool.Virginia.EDU/go/Whales/

Whales: A Thematic Web Unit is an integrated curriculum unit for use in grades 4–8. It provides cooperative lesson plans, teacher resources, and interactive student activities and projects. Links to related sites are also included.

Wind: Our Fierce Friend

http://sln.fi.edu/tfi/units/energy/wind.html

Wind: Our Fierce Friend, developed at the Franklin Institute Science Museum, is an interactive collaborative unit that investigates the science of wind energy. It contains lessons and activities for grades 4–6 and includes student contributions from online schools.

Year-Long Project

http://www.ed.uiuc.edu/ylp/units.html

The University of Illinois College of Education's **Year-Long Project** contains a wide variety of exemplary science units prepared by the pre-service teachers from 1994 to 1999 at the Urbana-Champaign campus. Science topics include the five senses, bats, electricity, insects, dinosaurs, rocks, vertebrates, simple machines, and weather.

Amateur Science

http://www.eskimo.com/~billb/amasci.html

Amateur Science contains hundreds of science activities, experiments, and projects for students and teachers in grades 4–12.

Annenberg/CPB Projects Exhibits Collection

http://www.learner.org/exhibits/

The **Annenberg/CPB Projects Exhibits Collection** covers a list of multimedia online interactive projects to enrich the K-12 curriculum. Science projects include Weather, Amusement Park Physics, Garbage, and Volcanoes.

Astronomy Picture of the Day

http://antwrp.gsfc.nasa.gov/apod/astropix.html

Astronomy Picture of the Day, for grades K–12, features a new picture of the universe each day with an informative explanation. The site also includes an archive of previous pictures dating back to 1995, a topical picture index, and related educational links.

Bad Science

http://www.ems.psu.edu/~fraser/BadScience.html

Bad Science, maintained by Alistair B. Fraser, dispels many popular misconceptions about science. The site, suitable for grades K-12, provides links to astronomy, chemistry, meteorology, and physics sites that attempt to sensitize teachers and students to examples of the "bad science" often taught in schools and universities and offered in popular articles and some textbooks.

BBC Online: Kids Health

http://www.bbc.co.uk/health/kids/

This UK site explores mental and physical health using simple printable activities, anatomy lessons, information about health issues, and helpful advice. There is also a cool Shockwave body tour.

Beakman's Electric Motor

http://fly.hiwaay.net/~palmer/motor.html

Chris Palmer's **Beakman's Electric Motor** provides simple illustrated directions that shows children in grades 4-9 how to make an electric motor from ordinary household items. Scroll to **Other Links** to find a good Spanish translation of this site.

Berit's Best: Environment Sites for Kids

http://www.beritsbest.com/SeriousStuff/Environment/

Berit's Best offers a growing collection of educational sites on the environment for elementary school children.

Biology Project

http://www.biology.arizona.edu/

The **Biology Project**, developed at the University of Arizona, is an interactive online resource for learning biology suitable for AP biology high school students. Topics consist of biochemistry, cell biology, chemicals and human health, immunology, Mendelian genetics as well as cell, human, molecular biology. Several of the topics include Spanish versions.

Bizarre Stuff You Can Make in Your Kitchen

http://freeweb.pdq.net/headstrong/control.htm

Bizarre Stuff You Can Make in Your Kitchen, created by Brian Carusella for grades 3-9, provides a warehouse of more than 100 science projects and experiments from clouds in a bottle to making an electric motor. You can view all the projects by category or in an alphabetical index.

BrainPOP

http://brainpop.com/

BrainPOP, developed by Dr. Avraham Kadar, presents animated movies, comics, experiments, quizzes and fun facts for kids ages 6 to 14. Topics include asthma, acne, blood, cancer, the brain, cells, hair, the skeleton, teeth and others. It makes learning science fun!

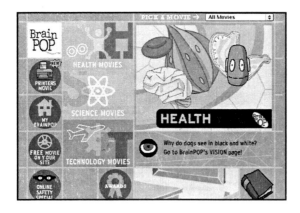

CBC 4 Kids` Laboratory

http://www.cbc4kids.ca/regular/the-lab/

Canadian Broadcasting Corporation (**CBC**) provides a wide variety of engaging science activities for grades 2-6. Children can take a virtual trip into space exploring the planets, playing space games, or finding answers to puzzling questions about the universe. They can also take fun science quizzes discovering weird news from the world of science, do their own science experiments, make a paper airplane, or investigate the Big Bang.

CELLS Alive!

http://cellsalive.com/

CELLS Alive! provides information on viruses, bacteria, human cells, and parasites for grades 7-12. The site includes images and videos of microorganisms that make you sick, and the blood cells that do battle to keep you well, such as white blood cells attacking an invader. You'll find biocams for viewing biological activity in real time and links to sites offering further information on microbiology, infectious diseases, and cell biology.

Comets and Meteor Showers

http://comets.amsmeteors.org/

Gary Kronk's **Comets and Meteor Showers,** sponsored by the American Meteor Society, provides information and pictures of comets and meteors for grades 5-12.

Discover Magazine

http://www.discover.com/

Discover Magazine provides an educator's guide for each issue offering the latest science news for grades 9-12. It also includes a picture gallery, selected sites, and Ask Discover where students can get answers from science experts.

Discovery Channel Online

http://www.discovery.com/

Discovery Channel Online provides a treasure trove of activities for enriching the science curriculum in grades 4-12. You can listen to online or read many interesting stories, take part in daring expeditions, view live cams, or use the guides to find information about animals, extreme weather, space, and other science topics.

Earth & Sky Radio Series

http://earthsky.com/

Earth & Sky Radio Series is a daily, two-minute radio science program for students in grades 6-12. It can be heard through RealAudio and features popular science topics, including climate and earthquakes. The site also includes a Teacher's Lounge with tips for using *Earth & Sky* in your classroom and a list of Web resources such as Ask the Experts page. In addition, kids will find fun science activities.

Earthquake Information from USGS

http://quake.wr.usgs.gov/

The United States Geological Survey (**USGS**) provides daily and weekly quake reports, geophysical and preparedness information, and other background information on earthquakes.

ENC!

http://enc.org/

The Eisenhower National Clearinghouse (**ENC**) provides K-12 teachers with a central source of information on mathematics and science curriculum materials. The site offers online publications, recommended mathematics and science lessons, activities, and Internet sites, ideas for educational reform concerning equity and standards and frameworks.

Electric Club

http://www.schoolnet.ca/general/electric-club/e/

The **Electric Club** presents an activities handbook of 37 experiments and projects in electricity and electronics for grades 6–12. Each experiment is divided into five components: The experiment, connections, challenge questions, flash facts and teacher's notes.

The Electronic Zoo

http://netvet.wustl.edu/e-zoo.htm

Ken Boschert's **Electronic Zoo** features a comprehensive catalog of pictures and information about animals for grades K-12. Scroll and click Animals to find hundreds of animal resources from amphibians to zoo animals in 22 classifications.

eNature.com

http://enature.com/

The **eNature.com** online field guide is a searchable database for identifying more than 4,000 plant and animal species of North America. Additional species and other nature content is constantly added to the database. The species accounts are from the bestselling National Audubon Society Field Guides, Regional Guides, and Nature Guides, published by Alfred A. Knopf.

Energy Quest

http://www.energy.ca.gov/education/

Energy Quest, from the California Energy Commission, provides a vast collection of activities, organized by difficulty levels, for teaching about energy in grades K-12. Scroll and click Science Projects, Percy's Puzzles, or Poor Richard's Energy Almanac to find some of these classroom activities.

Exploratorium Science Snacks

http://www.exploratorium.edu/snacks/

Exploratorium Science Snacks provides an online collection of hundreds of experiments designed by science teachers for grades 4–12. All the snacks can be viewed in an alphabetical list, or viewed by subject area. The experiments are adapted from the *Hands-On Sciences* books published by the Exploratorium Museum in San Francisco.

Explore Science

http://explorescience.com/

Raman Pfaff's **Explore Science** is a multimedia extravaganza illustrating the laws of physics for students in grades 7-12. It is a Shockwave-laden experience of sights, sounds, and interaction with scientific theory. The site provides a collection of interactive explorations for astronomy, mechanics, electricity and magnetism, life science, waves, optics, and other science topics.

Explore the GLOBE Program

http://www.globe.gov/fsl/welcome.html

Global Learning and Observations to Benefit the Environment (**GLOBE**) is a worldwide network of students, teachers, and scientists working together to study and understand the global environment. Students and teachers from hundreds of schools and countries are working with research scientists to learn more about our planet. Research topics include atmosphere, biology, global positioning, hydrology, and soil investigations.

Exploring Planets in the Classroom

http://www.soest.hawaii.edu/SPACEGRANT/class_acts/

Exploring Planets in the Classroom features more than 25 classroom-ready pages of hands-on activities for geology, earth, and planetary sciences for grades 5-12.

The Faces of Science: African Americans in the Sciences

http://www.princeton.edu/~mcbrown/display/faces.html

The Faces of Science: African Americans in the Sciences presents more than 100 profiles of African Americans who have contributed to the advancement of science and engineering. Profiles are grouped by academic discipline and arranged in an alphabetical list. The site is appropriate for grades 5–12.

Family Explorer

http://members.nbci.com/almathea/FE/

Family Explorer is a monthly newsletter containing hands-on science and nature activities for students in grades K–6. To find classroom activities from past issues, click on **More Activities**.

The Froggy Page

http://www.frogsonice.com/froggy/

The Froggy Page is a comprehensive collection of resources about frogs for grades K-12. It includes pictures, sounds, tales, and songs. To find two online dissection projects, scroll to the Scientific Amphibian section of the page, locate Anatomy and Dissection, and click Whole Frog Project and Frog Dissection Tutorial.

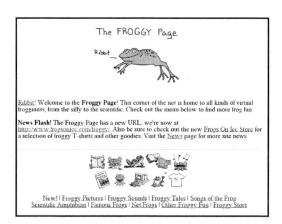

Fun Science Gallery

http://funsci.com/

The **Fun Science Gallery**, suitable for grades 7-12, is a collection of scientific instruments and experiments to make at home or at school. Projects include instructions for making telescopes, microscopes, batteries, sidereal indicators, and several other instruments.

Hands-On Technology Program

http://www.galaxy.net/~k12/

The **Hands-On Technology Program** provides a collection of more than 38 science experiments and hands-on activities for grades K–8. To find the list of experiments, click on subject. All the experiments are designed to be done with ordinary, inexpensive materials, and each experiment includes photocopyable sheets, teachers' notes, and materials needed.

Heart Preview Gallery

http://sln2.fi.edu/biosci/preview/heartpreview.html

The **Heart Preview Gallery**, created by the Franklin Institute Science Museum, presents an online interactive tour showing how the heart works. It is accompanied by activities suitable for grades 4–8. To find the activities, click Learn or Do in the picture of the heart.

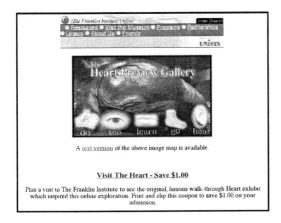

Helping Your Child Learn Science

http://www.ed.gov/pubs/parents/Science/

Helping Your Child Learn Science, prepared by the U.S. Department of Education, provides a collection of hands-on science activities for parents, teachers, and students ages 6–12.

Hewlett Packard Science Experiments

http://www.cvsd.org/greenacreselem/science.htm

Mark Johnson of **Hewlett Packard** provides hundreds of activities and experiments for chemistry, motion, light, sound, electricity and magnetism, and other science topics that can be used in any K–8 science curriculum.

HHMI's BioInteractive

http://biointeractive.org/

The Howard Hughes Medical Institute's (**HHMI's**) Web site is filled with bio activities and tools for students of all ages. For younger children, choose "Cool Science for Curious Kids." For older students, especially AP students, access the latest virtual tools for the geneticist, physician, and immunologist in the virtual labs. Also, visit Teacher Resources and under the pull down menu check out the online publication, "Seeing, Hearing, and Smelling", a guide to world of the senses and the nervous system.

The Hitchhikers Guide to Model Rocketry

http://library.advanced.org/10568/

The Hitchhikers Guide to Model Rocketry provides step-by-step tutorial that middle school students can use to build and design their first rockets. The site includes information on the principles of scientific rocketry in the Aerodynamics section, as well as other related links.

How Stuff Works

http://howstuffworks.com/

Marshall Brain's **How Stuff Works** provides a series of illustrated articles explaining the principles behind many devices from cell phones and modems to air conditioners and refrigerators for grades 4-12. You can ask a question, read answered questions, or subscribe to a free monthly online newsletter.

How Things Work

http://rabi.phys.virginia.edu/HTW/

How Things Work explains a wide range of physics concepts and laws from seesaws to copy machines to tape recorders to superconductors, and to roller coasters using everyday life examples. You can submit your physics questions and get answers from the author, Louis A. Bloomfield, a physics professor at the University of Virginia. The site is based on his book *How Things Work: The Physics of Everyday Life*, which answers hundreds of science questions. The site is suitable for grades 6-12.

Hubble Space Telescope Public Pictures

http://www.stsci.edu/EPA/Pictures.html

Hubble Space Telescope (HST) Public Pictures, for grades K-12, contains collections of spectacular pictures of celestial objects, each accompanied by brief descriptions. The site includes pictures organized by subject, 1994-2000 releases, HST's Greatest Hits Updated 1990-1998 Picture Gallery, and HST's Greatest Hits 1990-1995 Picture Gallery.

Interactive Physics and Math with Java

http://www.lightlink.com/sergey/java/

Sergey A. Kiselev created 23 Java applets for demonstrating high school physics concepts.

Katerpillars (& Mystery Bugs)

http://www.uky.edu/Agriculture/Entomology/ythfacts/entyouth.htm

The University of Kentucky Entomology Department provides a variety of insect projects for elementary school children. The site also includes a teacher/parent category with teaching ideas and materials.

Learning From the Fossil Record

http://www.ucmp.berkeley.edu/fosrec/fosrec.html

Learning From the Fossil Record provides online resources and a collection of paleontology activities for students and teachers in grades K-12. Check the standards matrix to find the grade levels identified for each activity.

LookLearn&Do: Projects

http://looklearnanddo.com/documents/projects.html

LookLearn&Do provides more than 40 project ideas that test scientific principles ranging from greenhouses and blimps to kites and mousetrap cars for grades 2-5.

MAD Scientist Network

http://www.madsci.org/

The **MAD Scientist Network**, housed at Washington University Medical School in St. Louis, is a collective cranium of scientists from various disciplines providing answers to your questions. From their Ask-A-Scientist archive, you can browse thousands of previously answered questions. In the Mad Labs, you'll find a collection of edible/inedible experiments that require nothing more than rummaging through your kitchen cabinets. The site also provides a comprehensive collection of science sites.

MAST

http://matse1.mse.uiuc.edu/~tw/home.html

Materials Science and Engineering **(MAST)** project from the University of Illinois, Urbana/Champaign provides a collection of low-cost laboratory experiments and other resources to teach high school students about the scientific principles of materials. Modules include ceramics, polymers, semiconductors, composites, concrete, metals, and energy. Each module contains lab activities, equipment list, a glossary, a quiz, and scientific information on the topic.

MathMol K-12 Activity Page

http://www.mathmol.com/

MathMol K-12 Activity Page serves as a starting point for those interested in learning about the field of molecular modeling and its relationship to mathematics.

McREL's Whelmers

http://www.mcrel.org/whelmers/

McREL's Whelmers are 20 eye-catching hands-on science experiments for grades K-12. Each activity is aligned to the National Science Education Standards. The material is from Steve Jacobs' book *Whelmers*.

Microworlds: Exploring the Structure of Materials

http://www.lbl.gov/MicroWorlds/

Microworlds: Exploring the Structure of Materials is an interactive tour of current research in the materials sciences at Lawrence Berkeley National Laboratory's Advanced Light Source. To start your tour, scroll and click Contents to find online activities appropriate for students at the high school level.

Mr. Biology

http://www.sc2000.net/~czaremba/

Mr. Biology, created by Charles Zaremba, offers an online Biology I and AP curriculum, explanations, worksheets, biological pictures archive, related links, and homework help to high school biology students.

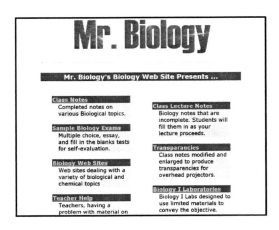

National Aeronautics and Space Administration

http://www.nasa.gov/

The **National Aeronautics and Space Administration (NASA)** provides a wealth of science resources for grades K-12. Among the resources, you'll find featured cool NASA sites. In the panel, you'll also find links to Earth and space sites, a collection of NASA sites just for children, and student and teacher educational resources. To find the site for each of the NASA field centers, click Welcome to NASA Web.

NASA's Kids

http://kids.msfc.nasa.gov/

NASA's Marshall Space Flight Center provides animated stories, space quizzes picture and word puzzles, a calculator find out what you'd weigh on the moon, and a Space Cadet Academy for learning about space exploration. The site is suitable for elementary school kids.

NASA Quest

http://quest.arc.nasa.gov/home/

NASA Quest provides support and services to K-12 schools, teachers, and students. To find classroom activities, select the SiteMap and click on Teachers' Lounge or Kids' Corner at bottom of the page.

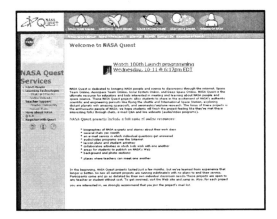

NASA Spacelink

http://spacelink.nasa.gov/

NASA Spacelink, an aeronautics and space teacher resource since 1988, provides a wealth of online and activities for grades K-12. Click on the Library to find a treasury of instructional materials. The site also includes a search engine to help you find educational NASA resources.

National Science Teachers Association

http://www.nsta.org/

National Science Teachers Association (NSTA), the leading professional science teaching organization provides a variety of resources for K-12 teachers. The site features information about sponsored publications, programs, and projects and also provides links to other online resources.

NERDS

http://nerds.unl.edu/nav/cont09.htm

Nebraska Educators Really Doing Science (**NERDS**) houses a library of more than 40 science demos for chemistry, physics, and biology, created by teachers for grades 7-12. To find this collection, click on Demonstration and scroll to Subject Specific. This page of science demonstration also contains more than 100 demos from other sites. Other resources includes an illustrated water rockets unit and 60-second QuickTime videos.

Neuroscience for Kids

http://faculty.washington.edu/chudler/neurok.html

Neuroscience for Kids, created by Professor Eric H. Chudler of the University of Washington in Seattle, is designed to help students learn more about the nervous system. Visit the Explore the Nervous System page to get information about the brain, the spinal cord, the neuron, the senses, and other related topics. To help you learn this nervous system information, click Experiments and Activities to find plenty of experiments, a coloring book, activities, and games. Included in this page is a collection of printable brain worksheets and lessons. The site is suitable for grades K-8.

New Scientist

http://newscientist.com/

This companion site to the *New Scientist* magazine contains articles, editorials, letters to the editor, selected science sites (hot spots) , bizarre entertaining tales, and other science information on a variety of topics for grades 8-12. The Last Word, a question-and-answer service, offers a searchable database of more than 700 answered questions on everyday science phenomena, such as why is the sky blue?, why does hair turn gray?, and do giraffes ever get hit by lightning?

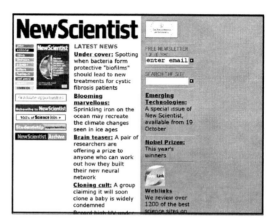

Newton's Apple: Science Try Its

http://www.pbs.org/ktca/newtons/tryits/

PBS's **Newton's Apple** provides a collection of Science Try Its experiments from season 9 to season 14 shows for grades 4-8.

Newton BBS

http://www.newton.dep.anl.gov/

The Argonne National Laboratory provides ask-a-scientist service for grades K-12 with an archive of more than 12,000 previously answered questions. The service includes an online form for submitting your science question. For other science activities, click on Teacher Classroom and Curriculum Development.

Northeast Fisheries Science Center

http://www.wh.whoi.edu/noaa.html

Northeast Fisheries Science Center, from Woods Hole Laboratory, provides middle and high school students with information about our living oceans. Click Fish Facts to find A Bouillabaisse of Fascinating Facts About Fish, including thousands of photos from the late 1800s to the present.

NOVA Online

http://www.pbs.org/wgbh/nova/

NOVA Online is a valuable resource for science teachers in grades 6-12. Unlike many Web sites that promote TV shows, this site presents hundreds of well-written articles derived from this venerable public television documentary series, including images and video clips. In addition, teachers will find lots of lesson ideas and online activities that can be used without the video tapes of the shows.

NSSDC Photo Gallery

http://nssdc.gsfc.nasa.gov/photo_gallery/

NSSDC (National Space Science Data Center) Photo Gallery contains hundreds of spectacular and popular photos of planetary, astronomical, and related objects for students in grades 4-12. The site also includes images of the solar system, objects taken by the Galileo spacecraft, the Hubble Space Telescope, and the Voyager 1 and 2 spacecrafts.

Nye Labs Online

http://nyelabs.kcts.org/flash_go.html

Nye Labs Online, the Internet home of Bill Nye for grades 4–8, now requires Macromedia's free Shockwave plug-in to access many of its updated features. Demo of the Day and Home Demos provide a collection of 40 experiments that teachers can print and recopy for their classrooms. Other new features include a Teacher's Lounge with information about the shows, a Goodies section with science videos, sounds, and photos, and Ask Bill Nye service where your science questions are answered weekly. Don't miss the catchy "Do you know thats." Try this one: "If you shouted on the moon, no one would hear you."

Optics for Kids

http://www.opticalres.com/kidoptx.html

Optics for Kids contains activities, experiments, and a selected bibliography for understanding the basics of light and lasers. The materials are appropriate for students in grades 5–8.

Physics 2000

http://www.colorado.edu/physics/2000/

Physics 2000 from the University of Colorado at Boulder provides animated science demonstrations for high science students and teachers. The site takes you on an interactive journey through modern physics where you can learn about Einstein's Legacy on X-rays, microwave ovens, lasers, and many other modern devices. You can also visit an Atomic Lab to see some surprising 20th-century physics experiments.

Questacon: Fun Zone

http://www.questacon.edu.au/fun_zone.html

Questacon, a children's science and technology museum in Canberra, Australia, provides a Fun Zone for elementary school children. The site includes a collection of hands-on experiments, online space and dinosaur activities, and incredible illusions.

Quick and Easy Activities

http://www.eecs.umich.edu/~coalitn/sciedoutreach/funexperiments/quickndirty/quickneasy.html

The Southeastern Michigan Math-Science Learning Coalition provides a wide variety of more than 200 hands-on activities and fun experiments for grades K-12. The activities are categorized by preschool, early elementary, later elementary, middle school, and high school levels.

Rain or Shine: Explorations in Meteorology

http://www.caps.ou.edu/CAPS/teacher.html

The Center for Analysis and Prediction of Storms (CAPS) at the University of Oklahoma provides a variety of hands-on weather activities accompanied by printable worksheets for K-12 students. The site includes a Teacher's Guide.

Rainforest Action Network

http://www.ran.org/

Rainforest Action Network (RAN) has been working since 1985 to protect the earth's rain forests and support the rights of its inhabitants. RAN's site provides many online science-education resources. Click Kids' Action Team to find classroom activities for use in grades K–8.

Reeko's Mad Scientist Lab

http://www.spartechsoftware.com/reeko/

Reeko's Mad Scientist Lab features a collection of science experiments sorted by categories from chemistry to sound delivered in a irreverent style for grades 4-12. The experiments are also organized by skill levels of easy, medium, and hard.

Safari Touch Tank

http://oberon.educ.sfu.ca/projects/safari/ 3DTouchTank/3dlib/tank.html

Safari Touch Tank, created at Simon Fraser University for grades 4–8, is a clickable undersea onscreen aquarium at which kids can click an item to find a description about it, use an online dictionary to learn its definition/pronunciation, see it enlarged, or view a short animation about it. The site includes an gallery of all the images used in the aquarium and a QuickTime video.

SandlotScience.com

http://sandlotscience.com/

SandlotScience.com is an online collection of colorful optical illusions for grades 4-12 without a lot of "deep" science. The site includes many interactive demonstrations, science projects, puzzles, and related links.

Science Activities Index

http://sln.fi.edu/tfi/activity/act-summ.html

Science Activities Index, from the Franklin Institute, is a collection of more than 40 K-8 science activities arranged by subject and grade level. Activity topics include heartbeat, the earth bowl, ocean in a bottle, clear as crystal, and spinning satellites.

Science Explorer

http://www.exploratorium.edu/science_explorer/

Science Explorer from the Exploratorium contains a variety of hands-on activities with step-by-step instructions that elementary kids can do at home. At the bottom of the each experiment's page, click on Ken Finn if you want to send him a message about your results and discoveries.

Science Friday Kids Connection

http://www.npr.org/programs/sfkids/

NPR's **Science Friday Kids Connection** provides a variety of science-related topics for grades 6-12. The show archives offer an online library of previous broadcasts that you can listen to through RealAudio. Each episode is accompanied by classroom materials that include a synopsis, selected references, student questions, a class project, experiments, and links to related sites.

Science is Fun

http://www.scifun.chem.wisc.edu/

Bassam Z. Shakhashiri, a Professor of Chemistry at the University of Wisconsin at Madison, shares the fun of science through home science activities, chemical demonstrations, and general chemistry information for grades 5-12.

Science Playwiths

http://www.ozemail.com.au/~macinnis/scifun/

Peter Macinnis' **Science Playwiths** provides a wide variety of fun science experiments that can be made with everyday things for grades K-8. Topics consist of bubbles, earthy things, electricity and magnetism, fluid flow, gases and liquids, making things, mini-experiments, kitchen chemistry, physics for living things, science quickies, open-ended questions, sight and light things, living things, and sound. Each experiment includes a simple explanation that is linked to "This will help you understand."

Science Resource Center

http://chem.lapeer.org/

Science Resource Center, created by Patrick M. Gormley, provides high school science teachers with demonstrations, laboratory investigations, and teaching tips for chemistry, biology, life science, and physics.

The Scientist

http://tc.unl.edu/rbonnstetter/60ss.htm

The Scientist Web site contains QuickTime movies from weekly programs hosted by Dr. Ronald J. Bonnstetter of the University of Nebraska. Each video explains and illustrates a scientific principle for elementary school students.

Scientific American

http://www.sciam.com/

Scientific American contains enhanced versions of print articles, explorations of recent developments in the news, interviews, ask the experts, and much more for students and teachers in grades 9-12.

SciQuest Foundation's K-12 Science

http://www.sciquestfoundation.org/k12/

The **SciQuest Foundation** provides extensive collection of K-12 science sites from lesson plans and experiments to human body atlases and games/puzzles.

SeaWiFS Project

http://seawifs.gsfc.nasa.gov/SEAWIFS.html

SeaWiFS Project, provided by NASA's Goddard Space Flight Center, features a high school Teacher's Guide that includes online activities for the study of ocean color from space. Topics include life in the ocean, the ocean isn't just blue, phytoplankton, the earth, and carbon.

SeaWorld/Busch Gardens Animal Resources

http://www.seaworld.org/infobook.html

SeaWorld/Busch Gardens offers a wealth of information about animal life and our ecosystems for grades K-8. Animal Bytes helps kids locate quick information about a terrestrial or aquatic animals, Aquatic Safari helps kids find facts about this tropical ecosystem, and Ask Shamu provides answers to the most commonly asked questions about animal life. To find other animal information on such topics as killer whales, sharks, tigers, and tropical forests, click on an item in the yellow panel.

SEDS

http://www.seds.org/

Students for the Exploration and Development of Space (SEDS), contains a vast array of astronomy and astrophysics resources for grades 5-12. Included are the multimedia tour of our nine planet solar system and a galaxy page with more information about the solar system, space sciences, astronauts, and the future.

SERCC Education Center

http://water.dnr.state.sc.us/climate/sercc/education.html

The Southeast Regional Climate Center (**SERCC**) provides a variety of weather resources for grades 5-9. You'll find weather information by topic, Southern AER, an online quarterly bulletin with interactive student weather activities, and a severe weather page, a weather quiz, and links to other weather and environmental sites.

Space Place

http://spaceplace.jpl.nasa.gov/spacepl.htm

NASA's **Space Place** offers a variety of hands-on earth and space science activities and projects for elementary school children.

StarChild

http://starchild.gsfc.nasa.gov/

StarChild, created by the NASA Goddard Space Flight Center is a premiere astronomy resource for teachers and students in grades K-8. Presented in two levels, it contains pictures and information about our solar system, galaxies, space, the universe, and other astronomy topics.

Thinking Fountain

http://www.sci.mus.mn.us/sln/

Thinking Fountain, created by the Science Museum of Minnesota, is an interactive mural containing science activities and experiments for students in grades K-6. Click any item in the mural to explore an activity, or scroll to the bottom of the page and click A to Z for an alphabetical list of all items in the mural.

TRC Activities

http://www.lerc.nasa.gov/Other_Groups/K-12/TRC/TRCactivities.html

NASA Glenn Teacher Resource Center (TRC), located in Cleveland, Ohio, provides hands-on classroom activities for teaching about aeronautics and rockets in grades 7-12. TRC also includes an index of space terms.

U.S. Geological Survey's Learning Web

http://www.usgs.gov/education/

U.S. Geological Survey's Learning Web provides a collection of classroom activities, projects, and earth science resources for grades K-12.

UT Science Bytes

http://ur.utenn.edu/ut2kids/

UT (University of Tennessee) Science Bytes is a series of online articles about science topics suitable for students in grades K-12. Among the articles are MarsRocks, Mad About Marmosets, and Rhinos and Tigers and Bears—Oh My!

Vertebrate Animals Hotlist

http://sln.fi.edu/tfi/hotlists/animals.html

Vertebrate Animals Hotlist, prepared by the Franklin Institute, provides students in grades K-8 with more than 150 links to resources containing information, facts, and pictures about animals.

Views of the Solar System

http://solarviews.com/

Views of the Solar System, created by Calvin J. Hamilton in four languages, is an online guide of the solar system for students in grades 5-12. The site contains more than 220 Web pages of information and more than 950 pictures and animations of the sun, planets, moons, asteroids, comets, and meteoroids. The Contents link lists all of the site's pages and interactive activities.

Virtual Body

http://www.medtropolis.com/vbody/

The **Virtual Body** contains a collection of interactive presentations on the functions of the brain, the digestive system, the heart, and the skeleton of the human body for grades 4-12.

Volcano World

http://volcano.und.nodak.edu/

Volcano World is the premiere source of volcano information on the Internet for grades K-12.

Water Science for Schools

http://ga.water.usgs.gov/edu/

Water Science for K-12 Schools produced by the U.S. Geological Survey offers information on many aspects of water, along with pictures, data, maps, a glossary, and an interactive center where you can give opinions and test your water knowledge.

WaterWorks

http://www.omsi.edu/sln/ww/

WaterWorks, from the Oregon Museum of Science and Industry, contains activities for teaching about water pumps, siphons, and the operation of fountains. It also provides information and ideas for building fountains with simple materials.

Weather Channel

http://www.weather.com/

The **Weather Channel** provides forecasts for anywhere in the world. The site also offers weather education resources and classroom activities for grades 4-12. To find them, scroll and click on Learn More in the left blue panel.

WebElements

http://www.webelements.com/

WebElements, created by Mark Winter of the University of Sheffield in England, provides detailed information about every element in the periodic table for students in grades 7-12.

WhaleNet

http://whale.wheelock.edu

WhaleNet provides a compendium of resources about whales and other marine mammals for students and teachers in grades K-12.

Why Files

http://whyfiles.news.wisc.edu/

The **Why Files** is an online science news journal for grades 5-12. It presents weekly in-depth explorations of the science behind the headlines. For a list of previous science stories, visit the archives.

Windows to the Universe

http://www.windows.umich.edu/

Windows to the Universe provides a rich array of documents, including images, movies, animations, and data sets that explore the earth and space sciences for grades K-12. The Kids' Space section offers three levels and a variety of interactive activities.

Wonders of Physics

http://sprott.physics.wisc.edu/wop.htm

Physics Professor Clint Sprott provides online a *Physics Demonstrations* sourcebook with dramatic demos for motion, heat, sound, electricity, and other physics topics as well as experiments you can do at home from his popular **Wonders of Physics** program at University of Wisconsin. To find these materials, scroll to Additional Information. The site is suitable for high school science classes.

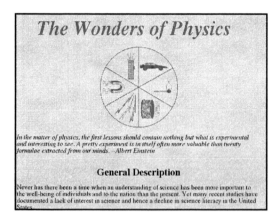

You Can

http://www.beakman.bonus.com/

You Can, by Jok R. Church, provides more than 40 science activities in the 50 Terrific ?s section for grades K–8. Activities in a question-and-answer format include "How does a lever make you stronger?," "Why do I hear weird sounds at night?," "How does yeast make bread rise?," and "What is thunder made out of?" The site also includes exciting interactive demos.

World in Motion

http://www.schoolnet.ca/general/worldinmotion/e/

World in Motion, created by the Society of Automotive Engineers (SAE), provides five science units for grades 4–8. Students learn how people, objects, and everyday things move around in our world. Each unit contains a series of simple, hands-on experiments that help to clarify the scientific principles.

WW2010 Online Meteorology Guide

http://ww2010.atmos.uiuc.edu/(Gh)/guides/

Weather World 2010, from the University of Illinois at Urbana-Champaign, provides an online meteorology guide featuring a collection of multimedia, Web-based instructional modules for grades 6-12. Topics include air masses, fronts, clouds, precipitation, El Nino, winds, hurricanes, severe storms, cyclones, and weather forecasting.

The Yuckiest Site on the Internet

http://www.yucky.com/

The Yuckiest Site on the Internet, presented by New Jersey Online, features the worlds of worms, cockroaches, and the human body for grades K–8. The site offers activities, information, and illustrations related to these topics.

Zoom School

http://www.enchantedlearning.com/school/

Enchanted Learning Software provides **Zoom School** with comprehensive online books about birds, dinosaurs, whales, sharks, and other science topics. The materials are designed for students of all ages and levels of comprehension. The site include printable worksheets, interactive quizzes, and dictionaries to accompany the books.

Boston Museum of Science Online Exhibits

http://www.mos.org/exhibits/online_exhibits.html

The **Boston Museum** presents a wonderful collection of online exhibits about Antarctica, archaeology, electron microscopes, electricity, fractals, Leonardo Da Vinci, and more. Exhibits include images, text, activities, audio and slide shows to make learning fun.

Discovering Dinosaurs

http://dinosaurs.eb.com/dinosaurs/index2.html

Discovering Dinosaurs from Britannica.com is an online exhibit about dinosaurs for grades 5-12. The activity guide introduces you to the dinosaurs as we know them today and show how theories about them have changed. Click on Enter this site to trace the great dinosaur debate through time by traveling down through each theme.

Exploratorium

http://www.exploratorium.edu/

Exploratorium provides a collection of online interactive exhibits and resources for teachers and students in grades K-12.

Franklin Institute Science Museum

http://sln.fi.edu/

The **Franklin Institute Science Museum** offers a variety of education resources for students and teachers in grades K-12.

Hands-On Science Centers Worldwide

http://www.cs.cmu.edu/~mwm/sci.html

Hands-On Science Centers Worldwide is a collection of interactive, public science museums from five continents. The site is appropriate for students in grades K-12.

John Donohue's National Park Photos

http://www.serve.com/wizjd/parks/parks.html

John Donohue's National Park Photos, for grades K-12, is a collection of photos of America's favorite national parks. Click Slide Show to view 30 of Donohue's favorite photos. To find links to additional resources, scroll to Other Park and Great Outdoors Pages .

National Air and Space Museum

http://www.nasm.edu/

National Air and Space Museum, for grades K-12, features a collection of exhibits and online resources about aviation and space science.

Natural History Museum of Los Angeles County

http://www.nhm.org/

Natural History Museum of Los Angeles County provides an impressive array of online exhibits, kid's stuff, and teacher materials for grades K-12. Click the site map to find these resources in the Education column.

New Mexico Museum of Natural History and Science

http://www.nmmnh-abq.mus.nm.us/nmmnh/

New Mexico Museum of Natural History and Science contains a wide variety of resources for students in grades K–12. Click Related Web Sites to find links to other online museums. To find classroom materials and activities for dinosaurs and mammals, click Research and Collections.

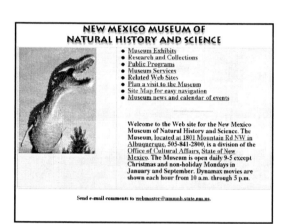

Science Learning Network

http://www.sln.org/

Science Learning Network (SLN) is an online collaboration among 12 international science museums providing hands-on activities for K–8 students. Click Explore Our Resources for a collection of interactive exhibits, and click news and links for other science resources from these museums.

Yahoo!: Science Museums and Exhibits

http://dir.yahoo.com/Science/ Museums_and_Exhibits/

Yahoo!: Science Museums and Exhibits is a directory of online science museums and exhibits, including aquariums and zoos.

Social Studies

Academy Curriculum Exchange

http://ofcn.org/cyber.serv/academy/ace/

Academy Curriculum Exchange includes more than 200 social studies lesson plans for elementary, intermediate and high school students.

American Civil War
(Teacher's Guide)

http://www.theteachersguide.com/
Civilwarlessons.html

American Civil War (Teacher's Guide) provides a variety of lesson plans, thematic units and teaching ideas for intermediate and secondary level students who are studying the American Civil War.

Amistad Case

http://www.nara.gov/education/teaching/amistad/
home.html

The National Archives and Records Administration presents the **Amistad Case,** a Supreme Court case in 1839 that involved a group of illegally-captured Africans who had seized their captors' ship and killed the captain. The subject has taken on new interest by the release of a major Hollywood movie. The site includes handwritten documents from the case and Teaching Activities designed to correlate to national standards for history, civics and government.

Anne Frank in the World,
1929–1945: Teacher Workbook

http://www.uen.org/utahlink/lp_res/AnneFrank.html

Anne Frank in the World, 1929–1945: Teacher Workbook is provided by the Friends of Anne Frank in Utah and the Intermountain West Region. It includes lesson plans and activities for grades 5–12, readings and overviews, timelines, and a glossary.

AskAsia

http://www.askasia.org

AskAsia, developed by the Asia Society in cooperation with several partners, offers high-quality, carefully selected resources for the classroom. Click For Educators and then Instructional Resources to find lesson plans, readings, and a resource center locator. All lessons, images, and maps have been copyright cleared and can be downloaded to use in the classroom. Lesson plan topics include Global, Asia-General, Asian American, Central Asia, China, India, Indonesia, Japan, Korea, the Middle East, Taiwan, and Vietnam.

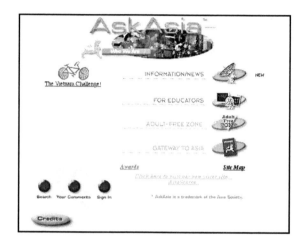

Awesome Library:
Social Studies Lesson Plans

http://www.neat-schoolhouse.org/Library/
Materials_Search/Lesson_Plans/
Social_Studies.html

The **Awesome Library: Social Studies Lesson Plans** presents a large number of links to a variety of lesson plans representing all areas of the K-12 social studies curriculum.

Beyond the Playing Field: Jackie Robinson, Civil Rights Advocate

http://www.nara.gov/education/teaching/robinson/robmain.html

Beyond the Playing Field: Jackie Robinson, Civil Rights Advocate, provided by the National Archives and Records Administration, features nine primary sources (including letters, telegrams, and photos), with accompanying lesson plans related to the documents. The lesson plans include objectives, materials, procedures, and follow up. Also featured are Robinson Quotes.

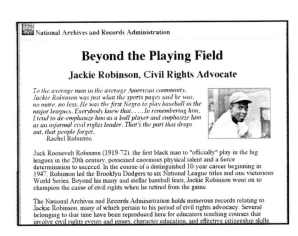

CEC Lesson Plans

http://www.col-ed.org/cur/

CEC Lesson Plans, sponsored by the Columbia Education Center based in Portland, Oregon, features a large assortment of lesson plans created by teachers for use in their own classrooms. Click Elementary (K–5), Intermediate (6–8), or High School (9–12) to find lesson plans to fit your needs.

Celebrations: A Social Studies Resource Guide for Elementary Teachers

http://teacherlink.ed.usu.edu/TLresources/longterm/LessonPlans/Byrnes/intro.html

Celebrations: A Social Studies Resource Guide for Elementary Teachers, developed by students at Utah State University, features lesson plans for 50 holidays and celebrations. Included are April Fool's Day, Cambodian New Year, Chinese New Year, Christmas, Cinco de Mayo, Columbus Day, Day of the Dead, Halloween, Hanukkah, Kwanzaa, Martin Luther King Day, Mexican Independence, Ramadan, Rosh Hashanah, and Thanksgiving.

China: Dim Sum: A Connection to Chinese-American Culture

http://www.newton.mec.edu/Angier/DimSum/DimSum%20T.ofCon.HomePg.html

China: Dim Sum: A Connection to Chinese-American Culture was developed at Angier School, Newton, Massachusetts. The site is a thematic, cross curricula, integrated resource for elementary classrooms which enhances awareness and understanding of Chinese-American culture while building basic academic skills. It includes Social Studies lesson plans and activities.

Connections+

http://www.mcrel.org/resources/plus/

Connections+ consists of K–12 lesson plans, activities, and curriculum resources provided by McREL. Social studies teachers can select from among these topics: Behavioral/Social Studies, Civics, Economics, Geography, History, and Multi-Interdisciplinary for links to lesson plans and activities.

Connecting Students: Internet Ready Activities and Lesson Plans

http://www.connectingstudents.com/lesson2.htm

Connecting Students: Internet Ready Activities and Lesson Plans assembles Web K–12 lesson plans and activities for students with computers. Topics include: American History, Geography, History, and Social Studies.

Cool Teaching Lessons and Units

http://169.207.3.68/~rlevine/coolunits.htm

Cool Teaching Lessons and Units is produced by Richard Levine, Tefft Middle School, Streamwood, Illinois. It provides a variety of resources, including examples of WebQuest units, ready made units and lesson plans, teacher resources, and help for building a teacher's own units.

Crossroads: A K–16 American History Curriculum

http://ericir.syr.edu/Virtual/Lessons/crossroads/

Crossroads: A K-16 American History Curriculum was produced by the Sage Colleges (Troy, New York) and the Niskayuna School District (Niskayuna, New York). The curriculum is composed of 36 units equally distributed among elementary, middle, and high school grade levels. Lesson plans and student worksheets are included.

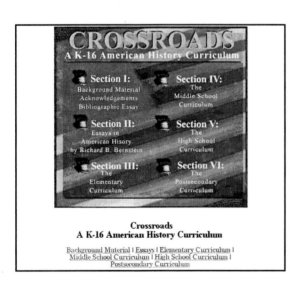

Crossroads
A K-16 American History Curriculum

Background Material | Essays | Elementary Curriculum |
Middle School Curriculum | High School Curriculum |
Postsecondary Curriculum

Curriculum of United States Labor History for Teachers

http://www.kentlaw.edu/ilhs/curricul.htm

Curriculum of United States Labor History for Teachers, sponsored by the Illinois Labor History Society, features 13 lesson plans that integrate labor history into the U.S. history curriculum from the Colonial period to the present.

Decoding the Past: The Work of Archeologists

http://educate.si.edu/resources/lessons/art-to-zoo/arch/cover.html

Decoding the Past: The Work of Archaeologists provides secondary school teachers with three hands-on lesson plans provided by the Smithsonian Institution enabling middle school and high school students to simulate the work of archaeologists. Also included are resources.

EconomicsMinute

http://www.econedlink.org

EconomicsMinute is a section of online lessons which feature links to newspapers and news channels, classroom discussion questions, and suggested classroom activities for helping students explore the economics behind the news of the week. Online lessons can typically be completed within a class period. To find the plans and activities, click on Current Economics Minute Lessons and Economics Minute Lessons Archive.

Economics and Geography Lessons for 32 Children's Books

http://www.mcps.k12.md.us/curriculum/socialstd/Econ_Geog.html

Economics and Geography Lessons for 32 Children's Books was developed by Patricia King Robeson and Barbara Yingling and is sponsored by the Council on Economic Education in Maryland and the Maryland Geographic Alliance. The site provides lesson plans suitable for grades 1–5. Included are objectives, vocabulary, materials, and teacher background.

EcEdWeb

http://ecedweb.unomaha.edu/teach.htm

EcEdWeb provides lesson plans and curriculum materials from the Economic Education Web site. The site's goal is to provide support for economics education from kindergarten through grade 12. Teacher's guides, lesson plans, and activities are featured.

Education World: Social Studies Lesson Plans

http://db.education-world.com/perl/browse?cat_id=1879

Education World: Social Studies Lesson Plans contains more than 150 social studies lesson plans, K-12, selected by Education World.

Flints and Stones: Real Life in Prehistory

http://museums.ncl.ac.uk/flint/menu.html

Flints and Stones: Real Life in Prehistory welcomes middle school students to the world of the Late Stone Age hunter-gatherers. Students explore this online world led by the Shaman, the leader of the Stone Age people.

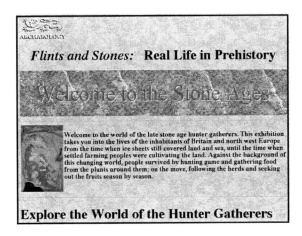

Florida Geographic Alliance Lesson Plans

http://multimedia2.freac.fsu.edu/fga/lessonplans.html

Florida Geographic Alliance Lesson Plans, from the Geographic Education and Technology Program of Florida State University, provides lesson plans for studies of various parts of the world (organized by continent).

Geography Lessons and Activities

http://www.nationalgeographic.com/resources/ngo/education/ideas.html

Geography Lessons and Activities is sponsored by the National Geographic Society. It provides lessons, units, and activities designed to bring good geography into the classroom. Click on Kindergarten-4th grade, 5th-8th grade and 9th-12th grade to find the lesson plans and activities of your choice.

Golden Legacy: Chinese Historical & Cultural Project Curriculum

http://www.kqed.org/ednet/school/socialstudies/golden/index.html

Golden Legacy: Chinese Historical & Cultural Project Curriculum provides lesson plans for a variety of topics. These include New Beginnings (Immigration, Chinatowns), Survival (Railroad Building, New Almaden Mine, Agriculture), Daily Life (Clothing, Bound Feet, Queues, Names), Traditions (Celebrations, Symbolism, Lunar Calendar), Education System (Writing System, Abacus, Tangrams, Folktales & Games, Puppetry), and Lasting Legacy (Postage Stamps, Conclusion).

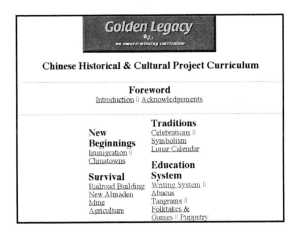

Government Lesson Plans from AskERIC

http://ericir.syr.edu/Virtual/Lessons/Social_St/Government/index.html

Government Lesson Plans from AskERIC includes more than 50 lesson plans in U.S. government, by topic and grade level for grades 3-12.

Internet CNN Newsroom

http://www.nmis.org/NewsInteractive/CNN/News-room/contents.html

Internet CNN Newsroom contains Teacher's Guides for middle and high school teachers to use with CNN's TV Newsroom Program. Teachers can videotape the program while they sleep (1:30 a.m.–2 a.m., Monday–Friday). Each episode usually presents five or six brief news stories with no commercials.

Japan Lessons: Lesson Plans for K–12 Teachers

http://www.indiana.edu/~japan/japan/mdnjapan/menu.html

Japan Lessons: Lesson Plans for K-12 Teachers contains objectives, materials, suggested classroom time, procedures, extension ideas, teacher background information, and student worksheets. To see all the lesson plans, click the Browse button.

Judges in the Classroom

http://www.courts.wa.gov/education/

Judges in the Classroom was developed under the auspices of the Washington State courts. Although the lesson plans found here were designed to help judges teach in K-12 classrooms, they can be adapted by social studies teachers with an interest in teaching about the law and the Bill of Rights. Click Elementary School Classrooms, Middle School Classrooms, or High School Classrooms to find the appropriate plans.

Learning Adventures in Citizenship

http://www.wnet.org/newyork/laic/lessons/lesson_menu.html

Learning Adventures in Citizenship presents more than 35 original lesson plans (K-12) that provide activities for good citizenship and which can be implemented on- or offline.

Lesson Plan Database

http://www.lennox.k12.ca.us/LPD.html

Lesson Plan Database presents 19 Native American thematic units for elementary pupils. The units were designed by Shayna Gardner of the Lennox (California) School District. Lesson plan topics include Cave Painting, Chumash Village, Sand Painting, Teepee Lesson, Nature Names, and more.

Lesson Plan Search

http://www.lessonplansearch.com/

Lesson Plan Search is a lesson plan search engine where teachers can search from over 1,600 lesson plans, including social studies, with more added weekly.

Lesson Stop

http://www.youthline-usa.com/lessonstop/index.html

Lesson Stop provides K-12 lesson plans for many school subjects including social studies. Also featured are advice on how to create lesson plans, links to other sites, and information on how teachers can subscribe to a newsletter.

Lesson Plans/Classroom Activities for Archaeology Themes

http://www.ties.k12.mn.us/~mayatch/mq96/lesson/Archaeology/

Lesson Plans/Classroom Activities for Archaeology Themes, from MayaQuest, will help social studies teachers plan fun, hands-on learning activities for grades 5–8. Featured topics include planting a time capsule or planning an archaeological dig.

Lesson Plans and Resources for Social Studies Teachers

http://www.csun.edu/~hcedu013/

Lesson Plans and Resources for Social Studies Teachers includes several hundred social studies lesson plans (K-12), online activities, teaching suggestions for current events lessons, and additional resource materials.

Lesson Plans/Classroom Activities for Hieroglyphics Themes

http://www.ties.k12.mn.us/~mayatch/mq96/lesson/Heiroglyph/

Lesson Plans/Classroom Activities for Hieroglyphics Themes, from MayaQuest, presents teachers of middle school students with a variety of lesson plans for teaching about hieroglyphics.

Lesson Plans for Teaching About the Americas

http://ladb.unm.edu/retanet/plans/soc/

Lesson Plans for Teaching About the Americas, provided by RETAnet, presents lesson plans written by secondary teachers. The plans are organized around these topics: Latin America Overview, Mexico, Indigenous Issues, African American and Caribbean Issues, Immigration, Geography, and Miscellaneous Subjects.

Mock Trial: The Titanic

http://www.andersonkill.com/titanic/facts.htm

Mock Trial: The Titanic is a site designed for teachers and students to participate in a mock trial involving the tragic story of the Titanic. The Teacher's Guide will help prepare the class for the trial by covering such issues as Assignment of Roles, Timing of the Trial, Legal Issues and Skills.

Mr. Donn's Ancient History Lesson Plans and Activities

http://members.aol.com/DonnandLee

Mr. Donn's Ancient History Lesson Plans and Activities was developed by Don Donn, a middle school teacher from Maryland. The site features detailed units, lesson plans, and activities for Early Man, Mesopotamia, Egypt, Greece, Rome, China, Japan, India, Africa, Aztecs, Mayans, Incas, and the Middle Ages.

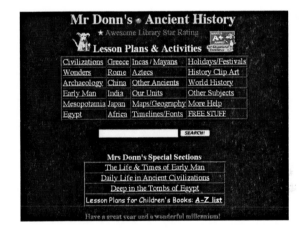

Mr. Donn's U.S. History Lesson Plans and Activities

http://members.aol.com/MrDonnHistory/American.html

Mr. Donn's U.S. History Lesson Plans and Activities (K-12) contains units, plans, activities and resources for teaching about Native Americans, Colonial Period and Revolution, Western Expansion, Civil War, Modern America Emerges, 20th Century and much more.

National Geographic Geography Lessons and Activities

http://www.nationalgeographic.com/resources/ngo/education/ideas.html

National Geographic Geography Lessons and Activities provides lessons, units, and activities designed to bring good geography into the classroom. Click Kindergarten-4th grade, 5th-8th grade, and 9th-12th grade to find the lesson plans and activities of your choice.

New York Times Learning Network

http://www.nytimes.com/learning/

New York Times Learning Network offers a daily News Quiz and Lesson Plan. Also included is a Lesson Plan Archive and Teacher Resources.

Nystromnet Geography Lesson Plans and Teaching Tips

http://www.nystromnet.com/lessonsandtips.html

Nystromnet Geography Lesson Plans and Teaching Tips contains quizzes; lesson plans for the primary, intermediate and high school levels; geography literacy games; and links to additional lessons in cyberspace.

Planning a Renaissance Faire

http://www.wre.liverpool.k12.ny.us/WRE/Featured_Projects/Renaissance%20Faire/sixrenid.html

Planning a Renaissance Faire was developed by Mrs. Mainzer, a sixth grade teacher. She provides suggestions for creating an interdisciplinary unit, The Renaissance Faire. Topics include: List of Renaissance Characters, Renaissance Craft Booths, Madrigal Dinner Menu, Renaissance Character Report Written By Sixth-Grade Students, Scenes From The Renaissance Faire, and Interdisciplinary Renaissance Unit Preparation for teachers.

Primary Sources and Activities

http://www.nara.gov/education/teaching/teaching.html

Primary Sources and Activities provides secondary school teachers with reproducible primary documents from the holdings of the National Archives of the United States, with accompanying lesson plans correlated to the National History Standards. Among the many lesson plans are (1) Jackie Robinson: Beyond the Playing Field, (2) The Zimmermann Telegram, 1917, (3) Constitutional Issues: Separation of Powers—Franklin D. Roosevelt's attempt to increase the number of Justices on the Supreme Court—and (4) Constitutional Issues: Watergate and the Constitution. Additional links to primary source documents are also included.

Social Studies Lesson Plans

http://www.uiowa.edu/~socialed/pages/lessons.htm

Social Studies Lesson Plans were developed by students and faculty of the University of Iowa College of Education for grades 9-12. The plans are organized in terms of the ten themes devised by the National Council for the Social Studies. Each plan consists of purpose, goals, materials, procedures, assessment, extensions, and resources.

South Carolina: Lessons From the Holocaust

http://www.scetv.org/HolocaustForum/contents.html

South Carolina: Lessons From the Holocaust features 11 lesson plans, 34 student handouts, two series of taped interviews, a bibliography, and related sites to other curriculum resources.

Using Primary Sources in the Classroom

http://rs6.loc.gov/ammem/ndlpedu/primary.html

Using Primary Sources in the Classroom helps teachers enhance their social studies curriculum by providing suggestions for using authentic artifacts, documents, photographs, and manuscripts from the Library of Congress Historical Collections and other sources.

What Do Maps Show?

http://info.er.usgs.gov/education/teacher/what-do-maps-show/index.html

What Do Maps Show? offers lesson plans for four geography and map-reading lessons suitable for upper elementary and junior high school levels. Each lesson contains step-by-step procedures, hands-on student activity sheets, and reproducible maps. There is also a List of Materials link, which contains maps useful for teaching geography.

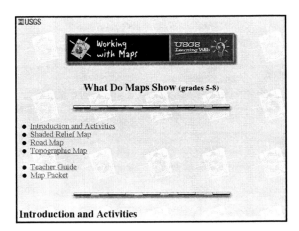

Abraham Lincoln Classroom Activities

http://www.siec.k12.in.us/~west/proj/lincoln/class.htm

Abraham Lincoln Classroom Activities was created by Tammy Payton's first-grade class. The site, suitable for the primary grades, includes an online quiz, an animation that shows the addition of states to the United States, a picture gallery of President Lincoln, a treasure hunt, suggestions for further classroom activities, and additional links.

Abraham Lincoln's Assassination

http://members.aol.com/RVSNorton/Lincoln.html

Abraham Lincoln's Assassination, a site organized by a U.S. history teacher, is appropriate for students in grades 6-12. The site features links to Ford's Theatre, the Mary Surratt House Museum, reproductions of newspapers reporting the assassination of Lincoln in 1865, Dr. Mudd, the life of John Wilkes Booth, and other interesting facts about Lincoln's assassination.

Advanced Placement Program

http://www.collegeboard.org/ap/subjects.html

Advanced Placement Program, provided by College Board Online, features tips for teachers and students, information about AP classes and exams, and related Web sites for all AP subjects including economics, European and U.S. history, U.S. and comparative government, and psychology.

Africa Online for Kids Only

http://www.africaonline.com/AfricaOnline/coverkids.html

Africa Online for Kids Only is a site where elementary and middle school students can read a Kenyan magazine written for kids, play games and decode messages, learn about the more than 1,000 languages in Africa, meet African students online, find a keypal, or just browse around.

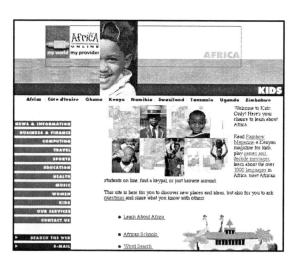

African-American History

http://www.geocities.com/djmabry/afro/afro.html

African-American History links to material on museums, newspapers, events, and people in black history, as well as numerous related links that rate the African American experience.

American Civil War Home Page

http://sunsite.utk.edu/civil-war/

The **American Civil War Home Page** contains general resources, graphic images, letters, diaries, and links to other reference sites.

American Memory

http://rs6.loc.gov/amhome.html

American Memory, drawn mainly from the special collections of the Library of Congress, has direct links to photographic, recorded sounds, manuscript, and early motion picture collections.

The American Presidency

http://www.grolier.com/presidents/preshome.html

The American Presidency, from Grolier Online, presents an exclusive history of presidents, the presidency, politics, and related subjects. The site includes encyclopedias, sound bytes, flip cards, and presidential quizzes. It is suitable for grades 6–12.

The American West

http://www.americanwest.com/

The American West focuses on the "Old West" and includes information on cowboys, Native Americans, pioneers and pioneer towns, explorers and more.

American Treasures of the Library of Congress

http://lcweb.loc.gov/exhibits/treasures/

American Treasures of the Library of Congress categorizes as "treasures" some of the more than 110 million items in the Library of Congress. These include Thomas Jefferson's handwritten draft of the Declaration of Independence, Jelly Roll Morton's early compositions, Maya Lin's original drawing for the Vietnam Veterans Memorial, the earliest known baseball cards, and the first motion picture deposited for copyright.

Anatomy of a Murder: A Trip Through Our Nation's Legal Justice System

http://tqd.advanced.org/2760/

Anatomy of a Murder: A Trip Through Our Nation's Legal Justice System puts students right in the middle of the action in a criminal murder trial. Included are an introduction, the story, relevant Supreme Court cases, a glossary, actual documents filled out in the course of an arrest, and links to other pertinent sites.

Anthropology on the Internet for K-12

http://www.sil.si.edu/SILPublications/Anthropology-K12/

Anthropology on the Internet for K-12 is a product of the Smithsonian Institution. It is an annotated listing of hot links to selected sites with information about the field of anthropology for teachers and young people. The sites are grouped under 11 different sections (including careers).

Architecture Through the Ages

http://library.advanced.org/10098

Architecture Through the Ages allows middle school students to learn about architecture from the great Maya to the building of cathedrals.

Ben's Guide To U.S. Government for Kids

http://bensguide.gpo.gov/

Ben's Guide to U.S. Government for Kids includes sections for grades K-2, 3-5, 6-8, and 9-12 which feature the U.S. Constitution, how laws are made, the branches of government, and citizenship. There is a separate section for parents and educators. Also included are games and activities, e-mail for children to ask questions and links to related sites.

Biographical Dictionary

http://www.s9.com/biography/

Biographical Dictionary, maintained by Eric Tentarelli, is an online dictionary that provides biographical information for more than 27,000 people from ancient times to the present day. It contains a searchable database and ideas for students and teachers on how to use the biographical dictionary as a classroom resource.

Black History: Exploring African-American Issues on the Web

http://www.kn.pacbell.com/wired/BHM/AfroAm.html

Black History: Exploring African-American Issues on the Web was created by Pacific Bell Knowledge Network Explorer and provides a wide variety of Internet-based resources that individual students or whole classes can use.

Blue Web'n Learning Applications

http://www.kn.pacbell.com/wired/bluewebn/

Blue Web'n Learning Applications, provided by Pacific Bell, includes lessons, activities, projects, resources, references, and tools for the K–12 teacher. Scroll to Content Table to find the History & Social Studies materials.

Capitals of the United States

http://www.scottforesman.com/resources/statescapitals/index.html

Capitals of the United States, provided by Scott Foresman, uses a game-like format for finding facts about the states and their capitals.

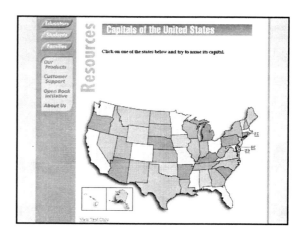

Celebrating the Life of Martin Luther King, Jr.

http://www.eduplace.com/ss/king/mlk.html

Celebrating the Life of Martin Luther King, Jr., from Houghton Mifflin, features activities and projects to help students of all ages explore the life and times of Dr. King. The site also includes links to other relevant resources.

CIA World Fact Book 1999

http://www.odci.gov/cia/publications/factbook/

CIA World Fact Book 1999 is a compilation of data about countries throughout the world.

Congressional E-mail Directory

http://www.webslingerz.com/jhoffman/congress-email.html

Congressional E-mail Directory provides the e-mail addresses of U.S. Senators and Representatives. You can click the address and write your lawmaker a letter.

Create a Newspaper!

http://www.twingroves.district96.k12.il.us/
NewspaperProj/Newspaper.html

Create a Newspaper!, designed by two Illinois teachers, provides an online activity for creating an historical newspaper. The site includes student assignments and Internet resources.

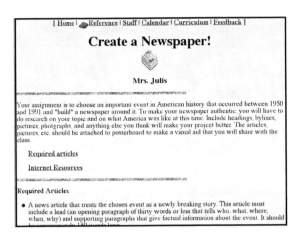

Cybrary of the Holocaust

http://remember.org/

Cybrary of the Holocaust is a place where you can share in teaching and learning about the Holocaust. You can journey through the Holocaust by interactive map, take a virtual tour of Auschwitz, and read diaries and interviews that can be used as background in teaching about this tragic historical event.

Donner Online

http://www.kn.pacbell.com/wired/donner/index.html

Donner Online is a Web-based activity in which middle and high school students learn about a topic by collecting information, images, and insights from the Internet, and then "pasting" them into a multimedia Scrapbook (a HyperStudio stack or a Web page) to share with others.

Educational Standards and Curriculum Frameworks for Social Studies

http://PutnamValleySchools.org/StSu/Social.html

Educational Standards and Curriculum Frameworks for Social Studies is an annotated list of Internet sites with K–12 educational standards and curriculum frameworks documents. It is maintained by Charles Hill and the Putnam Valley Schools in New York. The listings are by social studies organization and by state.

EduStock

http://tqd.advanced.org/3088/

EduStock is an educational Web page that can teach high school students what the stock market is and how it can work for them. It includes tutorials on the stock market and how to pick good stocks. The site also provides information on a select group of companies to help students start their research into what stock is going to make their fortunes. It also provides the only free real-time stock market simulation on the World Wide Web.

Egyptian Hieroglyphics

http://www.torstar.com/rom/egypt/

Egyptian Hieroglyphics is a site where Torstar Electronic Publishing Ltd. has identified the Egyptian phonograms that are closest to the English alphabet, and has created a way for students to translate between Hieroglyphs and English.

Exploring China: A Multimedia Scrapbook Activity

http://www.kn.pacbell.com/wired/China/
scrapbook.html

Exploring China: A Multimedia Scrapbook Activity permits middle and high school students to surf the Internet links at the site to find pictures, text, maps, facts, quotes, or controversies that capture their exploration of China. Students save the text and images they find important to create a multimedia scrapbook.

Famous American Trials

http://www.law.umkc.edu/faculty/projects/FTrials/ftrials.htm

Famous American Trials was developed by Doug Linder of the University of Missouri-Kansas City Law School. The site suitable for secondary school students presents 12 famous trials, including the Leopold and Loeb Trial, Scopes "Monkey" Trial, Rosenberg Trial, Amistad Trials, Salem Witchcraft Trials and the Scottsboro Trials. Also included are links to other trial resources, a Constitutional Trivia Quiz and Bill of Rights Golf.

Flints and Stones: Real Life in Prehistory

http://museums.ncl.ac.uk/flint/menu.html

Flints and Stones: Real Life in Prehistory welcomes middle school students to the world of the Late Stone Age hunter-gatherers. Students explore this online world led by the Shaman, the leader of the Stone Age people.

Footsteps to Freedom: Retracing the Underground Railroad

http://rims.k12.ca.us/ugr/

Footsteps To Freedom: Retracing the Underground Railroad features educators who accompany Southern Californians on the trails followed by fugitive slaves seeking freedom in Canada in the years before the Civil War. During the journey, the participants posted daily entries, photos, and reflections which will enrich students' understanding of this important phase of American History. The site also contains a "History of American Slavery and the Underground Railroad" and classroom resources.

From Revolution to Reconstruction and What Happened Afterwards

http://grid.let.rug.nl/~welling/usa/revolution

From Revolution to Reconstruction and What Happened Afterwards is an interactive American history textbook from the Colonial period to the First World War. It contains links to original sources and articles prepared by a number of contributors. Students can read the text sequentially or just go off on their own.

The Greatest Places

http://www.greatestplaces.org/

The Greatest Places takes students on an interactive educational journey to seven of the most geographically dynamic locations on Earth: Amazon, Greenland, Iguazu, Madagascar, Namib, Okavango, and Tibet.

Grolier Interactive World War II Commemoration

http://gi.grolier.com/wwii/

Grolier Interactive World War II Commemoration site includes the story of World War II, biographies and articles, air combat films to download, photographs, a World War II history test, and links to other resources.

Historic Audio Archives

http://www.webcorp.com/sounds/index.htm

Historic Audio Archives is a collection of sound clips from the past. It includes the voices of Senator Joseph McCarthy, President Richard Nixon, leaders in the Civil Rights movement, and others.

Homework Help

http://www.startribune.com/education/homework.shtml

Homework Help, sponsored by the Star Tribune Online, is a forum where a secondary student can ask a question about history, geography, government, current events, or other social studies topics. One of the Homework Help teachers who specializes in social studies will post a response.

HyperHistory Online

http://www.hyperhistory.com/online_n2/History_n2/a.html

HyperHistory Online includes more than 3,000 facts related to science, culture, religion, and politics. The site, appropriate for students in grades 7-12, also includes hundreds of color-coded lifelines of important persons and timelines for the major civilizations, accompanied by historical maps.

KidsClick!

http://sunsite.berkeley.edu/KidsClick!/midhist.html

KidsClick! features resources to enrich several social studies areas, including Archaeology, Prehistoric People, Ancient World, Ancient Egypt, Greece and Rome, The Vikings, Middle Ages, Knights, Rennaissance, Exploration, Pirates, American History (General), Revolutionary War, Civil War, Cowboys and the American West, World War I and II, and the Holocaust.

Let's Go! Around the World

http://www.ccph.com/

Let's Go! Around the World features online adventures to Africa, the Amazon rain forest and the Canadian Arctic; interactive projects directly linking students with children in different regions of the world; teacher resources; and the first-ever Amazon rain forest elementary school Web site.

Lewis and Clark: Where Cyberspace Meets the Unexplored West

http://www.nationalgeographic.com/features/97/west

Lewis and Clark: Where Cyberspace Meets the Unexplored West is a National Geographic Society site which allows middle and high school students to join the famous Lewis and Clark expedition. Their goal is to chart rivers, make friends with natives, open the West to trade, and look for a Northwest Passage. Additional features include a map to trace their progress, excerpts from the explorers' diaries, and a forum to share their own adventures with others online.

Living Africa

http://library.advanced.org/16645/contents.html

Living Africa features the people, the land, wildlife, and national parks. Also included are a wildlife conservation game, virtual postcards, virtual safari, an atlas, a quiz, a search engine, and links to other sites.

Lonely Planet

http://www.lonelyplanet.com/dest/dest.htm

Lonely Planet is an interactive clickable world map that allows students to travel to different countries around the world. When they arrive at their destination, they can click the slide show for loads of information, including facts, environment, history, economy, culture, and events enhanced with beautiful photos of the people.

Middle Ages: What Was It Really Like to Live in the Middle Ages?

http://www.learner.org/exhibits/middleages/

Middle Ages: What Was It Really Like to Live in the Middle Ages? is inspired by programs from The Western Tradition, a video series in the Annenberg/CPB Multimedia Collection. Middle and high school students can find information about religion, homes, clothing, health, arts and entertainment, town life, and related resources.

Name That Flag

http://www.futcher.com/nameflag/

Name That Flag is a geography contest suitable for grades 4–12. Students try to identify the country or origin of a flag and then enter their answers on an online form. A new flag is displayed after the current one is correctly identified. Names and home pages of winning entries are posted.

National Council for the Social Studies Online

http://www.ncss.org/

National Council for the Social Studies (NCSS) Online is the site of the professional organization representing social studies teachers in the United States. It is a showcase of teaching resources, professional development activities, publications, news, and Internet resources. It includes information on subscribing to a listserv for sharing ideas with other social studies teachers by e-mail.

NIE Online: Newspapers in Education

http://detnews.com/nie/index.html

NIE Online: Newspapers in Education, hosted by the *Detroit News*, provides online newspaper articles of interest to students in grades 5-12. Articles are accompanied by discussion questions and links to other relevant Web sites. An archive of previous articles is also included.

The 1920s

http://www.louisville.edu/~kprayb01/1920s.html

The 1920s, developed by Kevin Rayburn, features information about the "Roaring '20s." It presents a '20s Timeline, People and Trends and music of the era.

Odyssey in Egypt

http://www.website1.com/odyssey/

Odyssey in Egypt, developed by WebSiteOne and the Scriptorium Center for Christian Antiquities, was an interactive archaeological dig for middle school students. The site managers created, managed, transmitted, and served up pictures and text from Egypt on a weekly basis. Even though the project is no longer live, the information here can help history and geography teachers create interesting lessons.

Online Educator

http://ole.net/ole/index.shtml

Online Educator helps make the Internet an accessible, useful classroom tool. It includes super sites for teachers, search and browse features for lesson ideas in specific subjects, and a discussion forum.

The Oregon Trail

http://www.isu.edu/~trinmich/Oregontrail.html

The Oregon Trail is an online version of the award-winning documentary film aired nationally over PBS stations. It provides information, unusual facts, historic sites along the Oregon Trail, and a free teacher's guide containing classroom activities.

Perry-Castañeda Library Map Collection

http://www.lib.utexas.edu/Libs/PCL/Map_collection/Map_collection.html

Perry-Castañeda Library Map Collection was prepared by the University of Texas at Austin. It contains electronic maps of current and general interest for many regions of the world.

Port of Entry: Immigration

http://lcweb2.loc.gov/ammem/ndlpedu/activity/port/start.html

Port of Entry: Immigration offers the chance for students in grades 6-12 to assume the role of historical detectives. They search for clues to America's past in American Memory, the historical collections of the Library of Congress and investigate photographs and eyewitness accounts of immigrant life in America. For suggestions for using Port of Entry: Immigration, click on Teacher Materials.

SCORE History-Social Science Resources

http://score.rims.k12.ca.us/

SCORE History-Social Science Resources is part of the Network of Online Resource Centers in California linking quality resources from the World Wide Web to the California curriculum (K-12). The site includes resources that involve children in online activities. Suggested activities for effective use of the resources with students are included, as well as a search engine that allows you to search by grade level or by theme/topic.

Searching for China WebQuest

http://www.kn.pacbell.com/wired/China/ChinaQuest.html

Searching for China WebQuest is sponsored by Pacific Bell Knowledge Network. It allows your students to join a team and take on a role (foreign investor, human rights worker, museum curator, California state senator, or religious leader). The team members work together to create a special report that makes sense of the complex country that is China. The site also includes a Teacher's Guide.

Social Studies School Service

http://www.socialstudies.com/

Social Studies School Service has long been a leader in educational supplementary materials for the social studies. The organization now presents teachers with an online catalog, free teachers' guides, and links to other Web sites. Select the What's New button for a monthly feature focusing on an important social studies theme. Lesson plans and student exercises are included.

Spanish-American War in Motion Pictures

http://lcweb2.loc.gov/ammem/sawhtml/sawhome.html

Spanish American War in Motion Pictures, sponsored by the Library of Congress, presents films of the Spanish-American War and the Philippine Insurrection produced between 1898 and 1901. The films are displayed in QuickTime, .mpg and .avi formats.

Supreme Court Collection

http://supct.law.cornell.edu/supct/

Supreme Court Collection, sponsored by LII Legal Information Institute, contains information on recent decisions of the U.S. Supreme Court. The site also includes selected pre-1990 decisions, a gallery of the justices, and information on how to subscribe by e-mail to receive U.S. Supreme Court decisions only hours after their release.

Teaching Current Events Via Newspapers, Magazines and TV

http://www.csun.edu/~hcedu013/cevents.html

Teaching Current Events Via Newspapers, Magazines and TV offers lesson plans, activities and resources for making current events more productive and interesting in the K-12 classroom.

Teen Court TV

http://www.courttv.com/teens/

Teen Court TV (from the Court TV channel) is designed to give teenagers an inside look at the justice system. The program consists of three shows, including "What's the Verdict?," a one-hour show that invites teenagers to analyze real trials just as jurors do. Cases are picked that have already reached a conclusion, and the guests get to compare their verdicts to the ones actually reached in court. "What's the Verdict?" airs on Saturday and on Sunday at 1 p.m. All times are Eastern.

TIME 100

http://www.time.com/time/time100/index.html

TIME has profiled those individuals who — for better or worse — most influenced the last 100 years. They are considered in five fields of endeavor, culminating with the Person of the Century: Albert Einstein. Each profile contains historical information, photos, and audio messages.

Time Detectives

http://www.ilt.columbia.edu/k12/history/demquest1.html

Time Detectives get middle school students actively involved in analyzing historical materials for themselves. The first activity offers a diagram of a "mystery ship" and says "the remains of the ship also included many chains and iron rings." Students are asked to figure out what kind of ship it was based on that information. Other activities ask students to identify battles based on paintings; figure out the identity of a Revolutionary War soldier based on a found letter and to sort out Thomas Jefferson's apparent conflicting views on slavery and human rights by analyzing his writings.

TIME for Kids

http://www.timeforkids.com/TFK/

TIME for Kids, for grades 2-6, features information on people and events in the news, historic, profiles, a cartoon of the week, interactive talk, and online quizzes.

Turn-of-the-Century Child

http://www.nueva.pvt.k12.ca.us/~debbie/library/cur/20c/turn.html

Turn-of-the-Century Child is an online activity, developed for the middle school. Students study the life and times of children in the early 1900s as "junior" historians and use primary source material for critical inquiry. They assemble a physical and digital scrapbook of letters, oral histories, artifacts, diary entries, narratives and images to create an invented child within a family. For ideas on how to use this activity, click on Teacher's Lesson Plans.

U.S. Government Agencies Home Pages for Kids

http://www.odci.gov/cia/ciakids/govagency.html

U.S. Government Agencies Home Pages for Kids includes links to these Kids' Home Pages: The White House for Kids, The Federal Bureau of Investigation's Kid's and Youth Educational Page, the United States Air Force, the United States Department of State Digital Diplomacy for Students, the United States Department of Energy Education Community, the United States Treasury's Page for Kids, the Federal Emergency Management Agency's Page for Kids, and the National Aeronautics and Space Administration's Welcome to Kids.

U.S. House of Representatives

http://www.house.gov/

U.S. House of Representatives home page provides public access to legislative information as well as information about members, committees, and organizations of the House. The site includes links to other U.S. government information resources.

The United States Senate

http://www.senate.gov/

The United States Senate is a site that provides information about the members of the Senate, Senate committees, and Senate leadership and support offices. It also includes general background information about U.S. Senate legislative procedures, Senate facilities in the Capitol Building, and the history of the Senate.

The Valley of the Shadow: Living the Civil War in Pennsylvania and Virginia

http://jefferson.village.virginia.edu/vshadow/vshadow.html

The Valley of the Shadow: Living the Civil War in Pennsylvania and Virginia interweaves the histories of two communities on either side of the Mason-Dixon line during the American Civil War. The site, appropriate for grades 8-12, features pages from newspapers of the time, original census returns, diaries and maps, selected army rosters, photos, and commentary.

Vietnam: Yesterday and Today

http://www.oakton.edu/~wittman/

Vietnam: Yesterday and Today, prepared by Sandra M. Wittman, provides a chronology of the war and materials for study and teaching. It also has links to other relevant Web resources.

Weekly Reader Galaxy

http://www.weeklyreader.com/

Weekly Reader Galaxy, an online newspaper provided by the Weekly Reader Corporation, features social studies activities for students in grades K-6. These include news, polls, contests, games, and mystery photos.

Women in World History Curriculum

http://www.womeninworldhistory.com/

Women in World History Curriculum, directed by Lyn Reese, is an interactive site full of information and resources about women's experiences in world history. It includes female heroes, lesson plans, reviews of classroom materials, and links to other resources.

World Surfari

http://www.supersurf.com/

World Surfari allows elementary and middle school students to take a virtual "surfari" to a different country every month! The site is produced by Brian Giacoppo.

World War I Remembered–The Great War: 80 Years On

http://news.bbc.co.uk/hi/english/special_report/ 1998/10/98/world_war_i/newsid_197000/7437.stm

World War I Remembered—The Great War: 80 Years On, from the BBC, offers a 10-minute video collage of photos and newsreel footage, audio interviews of veterans, a selection of soldiers' letters home, and overviews of four major battles.

World War I: Trenches on the Web

http://www.worldwar1.com/

World War I: Trenches on the Web features information on people, places, and events that led to one of the tragic episodes in modern history. The site also includes a poster collection and reference resources.

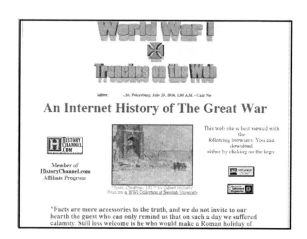

World War II: An American Scrapbook

http://tqjunior.thinkquest.org/4616/

World War II: An American Scrapbook was created as an entry in the Thinkquest Junior Contest by elementary school students from McRoberts Elementary School in Katy, Texas. You will find stories they collected about World War II from people close to them—their grandparents and great grandparents. They have also included three lesson plans to use with the stories.

World War II Commemoration

http://gi.grolier.com/wwii/

World War II Commemoration, presented by Grolier Online, features the story of World War II, biographies and articles, air combat films, photographs, a World War II history test, and World War II links.

World War II History Textbooks Project

http://www.ora.com/catalog/netlessons/excerpt/wit.html

World War II History Textbooks Project enables students to research and compare how events of World War II are treated in various countries' school textbooks through linking with another classroom from that country. The online activity is taken from the book Net Lessons: Web-Based Projects for Your Classroom by Laura Parker Roerden.

You Be the Historian

http://americanhistory.si.edu/hohr/springer/

You Be the Historian is an online activity where students examine primary sources to determine what life was like 200 years ago for Thomas and Elizabeth Springer's family in New Castle, Delaware. Also included are ideas for teachers using the activity in their classrooms with and without online connectivity. The site is appropriate for middle and high school students.

SOCIAL STUDIES   EXHIBITS AND MUSEUMS

Abraham Lincoln Online

http://www.netins.net/showcase/creative/lincoln.html

Abraham Lincoln Online presents historic Lincoln sites, resources, pictures, speeches, and writings, as well as a Lincoln Quiz-of-the-Month. You can also add your views to an online discussion.

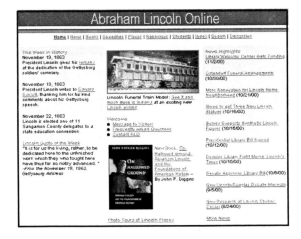

AFRO-Americ@'s Black History Museum

http://www.afroam.org/history/history.html

AFRO-Americ@'s Black History Museum, sponsored by AT&T, presents interactive exhibits appropriate for Grades 8-12. Topics include Black Resistance-Slavery in the U.S., Tuskegee Airmen, Jackie Robinson, Black Panther Party, Black or White, Million Man March, Scottsboro Boys, and This Is Our War.

The Ancient Olympic Games Virtual Museum

http://devlab.dartmouth.edu/olympic/

The Ancient Olympic Games Virtual Museum provides a plethora of information about these contests, the forefathers of our modern Olympic Games. The online museum includes a tour of the site, the story of a competitor, descriptions of the ancient events, a slide show of modern Greece, and related Web sites.

Benjamin Franklin: Glimpses of the Man

http://sln.fi.edu/franklin/rotten.html

Benjamin Franklin: Glimpses of the Man takes you to the Franklin Institute's online exhibit on this multitalented Founding Father.

Boston's Freedom Trail

http://www.std.com/homepages/std/
freedom.trail.html

Boston's Freedom Trail takes students through almost three centuries of Boston's colonial and revolutionary history. Included is a map, graphics, and an online guided tour.

Colonial Williamsburg

http://www.history.org/holiday/holiday.htm

Colonial Williamsburg features information on the life and times of colonial America. The site also includes a colonial dateline highlighting events from 1750 to 1783. It also has resources for teachers and students in Grades 5-12.

1492: An Ongoing Voyage

http://sunsite.unc.edu/expo/1492.exhibit/Intro.html

1492: An Ongoing Voyage is a Library of Congress exhibit of photos and discussions about Columbus' discovery of America.

George Washington's Mount Vernon Estate and Gardens

http://www.mountvernon.org/

George Washington's Mount Vernon Estate and Gardens provides a tour of our first President's home, library, and grounds. The site also includes links to additional resources.

The Library of Congress Exhibitions

http://marvel.loc.gov/

The Library of Congress Exhibitions lists exhibits, events, and services and provides information on how to use their online library for your own research.

Monticello: The Home of Thomas Jefferson

http://www.monticello.org/

Monticello: The Home of Thomas Jefferson allows you to follow Jefferson through his day and to use a clickable index to find information on a variety of matters relating to the third U.S. President.

Old Sturbridge Village

http://www.osv.org/

Old Sturbridge Village takes you back in time and lets you visit the largest historical museum in the Northeast. The museum, located in Sturbridge, Massachusetts, re-creates the daily work activities and community celebrations of a rural 19th-century town.

Pyramids—The Inside Story

http://www.pbs.org/wgbh/pages/nova/pyramid/

Pyramids—The Inside Story is sponsored by Nova Online. Students can wander through the chambers and passageways of the Great Pyramid, and learn about the pharaohs for whom these monumental tombs were built.

Spanish Missions of California

http://library.thinkquest.org/3615/

Spanish Missions of California is a place where teachers and students can find out who created the missions and why, take a tour of a typical mission, and learn about the people who lived there. Included is a page just for teachers and links to more places to find additional information.

United States Holocaust Memorial Museum Online Exhibitions

http://www.ushmm.org/exhibits/exhibit.htm

United States Holocaust Memorial Museum provides high school teachers and students with a series of online exhibitions relating to the history of the Holocaust.

Walking Tour of Plimoth Plantation

http://spirit.lib.uconn.edu/ArchNet/Topical/Historic/ Plimoth/Plimoth.html

Walking Tour of Plimoth (Plymouth) Plantation provides images and descriptions of the first permanent European settlement in southern New England, dating from 1620.

Welcome to the White House

http://www.whitehouse.gov/

Welcome to the White House offers a tour of our President's home. You can listen to speeches, view photos, search White House documents, and e-mail the president and vice president.

White House for Kids

http://www.whitehouse.gov/WH/kids/html/ home.html

White House for Kids introduces Socks, the First Cat, who leads children on a tour of the White House. They can learn about its history and about other children and pets who have lived there, as well as send e-mail to the president, vice president, and first lady.

Special Education

Award-Winning Teacher Achievement Lesson Plans

http://www.ashland.com/education/lesson_plans/week21/

This site is an excellent resource for special education teachers. It provides instruction on motivating students in grades 9-12. You'll find at the bottom of the page an archive of useful lesson plans.

British Columbia Ministry of Education—Special Education On-line Documents

http://www.bced.gov.bc.ca/specialed/docs.htm

British Columbia Ministry of Education—Special Education On-line Documents provides teachers with resources and teaching tips for working with special education students. Resources are available for teaching the visually impaired, those with a hearing loss, the intellectually disabled, the gifted, and students with a variety of chronic health conditions ranging from allergies to spina bifida.

Kodak Special Education Lesson Plans

http://www.kodak.com/global/en/consumer/education/lessonPlans/indices/specialEducation.shtml

Kodak provides a collection of photography lesson plans for use with special needs students.

Special Education Lesson Plans

http://www.geocities.com/Athens/Forum/6727/lessons.html

Special Education Lesson Plans provides 37 unit plans developed by teachers from elementary schools in Kansas City area for inclusion of students with special education needs in their classrooms. Primary topics include forest colors and shapes/sizes, and some intermediate topics are early America and deserts.

Thematic Planning Units

http://busboy.sped.ukans.edu/projects/theme/

Thematic Planning Units feature 21 primary and 16 intermediate units developed by teachers at the University of Kansas. Each unit consists of specific outcomes and objectives, activities, and followed by team planning pages. To view or print this material, you must download Adobe's free Acrobat free Reader.

The ARC of the United States

http://thearc.org/

The ARC of the United States, sponsored by the country's largest voluntary organization committed to the welfare of all children and adults with mental retardation, provides links to sites of interest to teachers and parents.

Awesome Library: Special Education

http://www.awesomelibrary.org/spec-ed.html

The **Awesome Library** provides an extensive collection of special education resources from assistive technology to developmental disabilities sites.

Blind Children's Center

http://www.blindcntr.org/bcc/

Blind Children's Center is a nonprofit organization available to blind and partially sighted children. The site provides information about educational preschool programs, social services, infant stimulation programs, and support and volunteer opportunities. Also provided are links to other relevant resources.

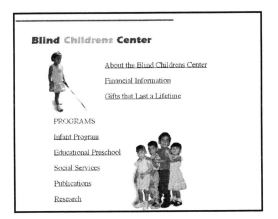

California's School-to-Work Interagency Transition Partnership

http://www.sna.com/switp/

California's School-to-Work Interagency Transition Partnership (SWITP) is a statewide effort to help students with disabilities to move successfully from school to work. The site provides links to information about employment and training resources, people who can provide technical assistance, information for parents and consumers, and links to additional resources.

Center for the Study of Autism

http://www.autism.org/

Center for the Study of Autism (CSA) provides information about autism to parents and professionals and includes several links to relevant resources for teachers.

Children and Adults with Attention Deficit Disorders

http://chadd.org/

Children and Adults with Attention Deficit Disorders (CH.A.D.D.) is a nonprofit, parent-based organization formed to better the lives of individuals with attention deficit disorders. The site provides links to resources for parenting, teaching, and treating kids who have this disability.

Children With Disabilities

http://www.childrenwithdisabilities.ncjrs.org/

The **Children With Disabilities** Web site offers families, service providers, and other interested individuals information about advocacy, education, employment, health, housing, recreation, technical assistance, and transportation covering a broad array of developmental, physical, and emotional disabilities.

Children with Special Needs

http://dent.edmonds.wednet.edu/IMD/
specialchild.html

Children with Special Needs is produced by Edmonds (Washington) School District. It provides links to a variety of special needs (K-12) from ADD to the visually impaired and includes a medical search engine. The site also provides information about computer adaptive software and wheelchairs.

The Council for Exceptional Children

http://www.cec.sped.org/

The Council for Exceptional Children (CEC) is the largest international professional organization dedicated to improving educational outcomes for individuals with exceptionalities, students with disabilities, and/or the gifted. CEC manages a number of grants, contracts, and research projects, including the ERIC Clearinghouse on Disabilities and Gifted Education.

Deaf World Web

http://dww.deafworldweb.org/

Deaf World Web features links to Web resources in 36 countries of the world and an alphabetical list of information about deaf culture.

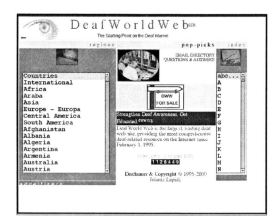

Disability.gov

http://disability.gov/

Disability.gov provides comprehensive information on U.S. federal programs, services, and resources for Americans with disabilities and their families.

Early Childhood Thematic Units

http://www.sbcss.k12.ca.us/sbcss/
specialeducation/ecthematic/

Early Childhood Thematic Units, appropriate for special education, incorporates technology throughout. They include ideas for bulletin boards, cooking, literature, fine and gross motor activities, language development, music, toys and materials, and software. Although most suitable for the preschool level, they can also be a source of ideas for teachers working with primary pupils. Some of the units are: The Zoo, At the Farm, Halloween, Thanksgiving/Foods, Transportation, and Insects.

Family Village: A Global Community of Disability-Related Resources

http://www.familyvillage.wisc.edu/index.htmlx

Family Village: A Global Community of Disability-Related Resources is a directory of resources covering disability issues on the Internet. It also provides a set of discussion lists and chat rooms.

The Federal Resource Center for Special Education

http://www.dssc.org/frc/

The **Federal Resource Center for Special Education** provides educators with the latest developments in special education.

Gallaudet University's National Deaf WWW Sites

http://www2.gallaudet.edu/
deafconnection_usadeaf.htm

Gallaudet University, a school for the hearing impaired and deaf in Washington, D.C., offers an extensive list of resources at its Deaf Connection Web site.

Gifted Resources Home Page

http://www.eskimo.com/~user/kids.html

Gifted Resources Home Page contains links to all known online gifted resources, enrichment programs, talent searches, summer programs, mailing lists, and early acceptance programs. More resources will be added as they become available.

HandSpeak: A Sign Language Dictionary Online

http://www.handspeak.com/

HandSpeak is an animated dictionary of sign language. The signs are grouped alphabetically and by categories. A new sign is added daily. It is a great introduction to sign language, a review of vocabulary for the deaf, a quick tutorial for parents or teachers of deaf children, or just fun for anyone interested in the topic.

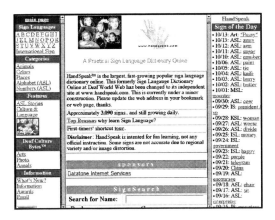

Internet Resources for Special Children

http://irsc.org/

Internet Resources for Special Children (IRSC) offers valuable information for parents, family members, caregivers, friends, educators, and medical professionals who interact with children who have disabilities. Provided are disability links, a search engine, and articles from local newspapers and school districts as well as those written by online media columnists.

LD Online

http://ldonline.org/

LD Online is an interactive guide to learning disabilities for parents, teachers and children. To find loads of instructional tips, enter the words "teaching strategies" in the search engine. The site highlights new information in the field of learning disabilities, has information on every aspect of learning disabilities, and features a comprehensive listing of learning disabilities events on the Internet. It also offers personal essays on first-hand experiences with the challenges of learning disabilities and audio clips from experts in the field.

National Information Center for Children and Youth with Disabilities

http://www.nichcy.org/

Developed by the National Information and Referral Center, this site provides information on issues and concerns related to disabilities for families and professionals. The focus of the information is on children and young adults.

National Federation of the Blind

http://nfb.org/

The **National Federation of the Blind (NFB)** is the largest organization of the blind in America. There are links to Braille literacy, government and community services, legislation, research, and technology.

National Institute on Deafness and Other Communication Disorders (NIDCD)

http://www.nidcd.nih.gov/

NIDCD, one of the National Institutes of Health, supports and conducts research "on the normal and disordered processes of hearing, balance, smell, taste, voice, speech and language." The site offers a variety of health publications on these and other communication disorder topics. Also, there's a glossary of commonly used medical terms associated with communicative disorders.

Parent Pals.com: Special Education

http://parentpals.com/5.0newsletter/Newsletter.html

Parent Pals.com offers a wealth of teaching strategies for students with special learning needs in the teaching games and weekly tips sections.

Special Education Resources on the Internet (SERI)

http://www.hood.edu/seri/serihome.htm

SERI is a collection of special education resources, including information about general disabilities, legal and law issues, physical and health disorders, and learning disabilities.

Sign Writing Site

http://signwriting.org/

Sign Writing Site provides sign-writing lessons as well as an online American Sign Language picture dictionary. The site also includes online versions of *Cinderella—Part One*, *Cinderella—Part Two*, *Humpty Dumpty*, and *Goldilocks and the Three Bears* written in English and American Sign Language for grades K-12.

Special Educator's Web Pages

http://www.geocities.com/Athens/Styx/7315/

Special Educator's Web Pages produced by Kay Smith of the Clark County (Nevada) schools, contains information useful to K-12 teachers, including lesson planning; grants; behavior management; research; statutes, regulations and case law; and free materials.

Special Needs Education Network

http://www.schoolnet.ca/sne/

Special Needs Education (SNE) endeavors to maintain a comprehensive and current Web directory of resources relating to special education. Select resources for a directory of specific disability topics, including dyslexia, attention deficit disorder, Down syndrome, and gifted education. For lesson plans, diagnostic tools, and other teaching and learning information, visit the teacher and parent resource area.

Teaching Ideas for Early Childhood Special Educators

http://www4.mcps.k12.md.us/schools/PEP/teach.htm

Teaching Ideas for Early Childhood Special Educators groups ideas according to themes. Also provided are a database of teaching ideas and links to other resources.

Web Resources for Educators

http://www2.gvsu.edu/~baleikok/teaching.html

Web Resources for Educators offers categorized general and special education links, including ADHD, assistive technology, autism, English as a second language, general disability information, hearing impairments, learning disabilities, lesson plans, visual impairments, and many other educational links.

Vocational/ Technical Education

Business Education Lesson Plans and Resources

http://www.angelfire.com/ks/tonyaskinner/
index.html

Business Education Lesson Plans and Resources contains plans and resources for Accounting, Business Law, Computers, Economics, General Business, Internet, Keyboarding, and Office Tech. There are also links to professional organizations and a job search section.

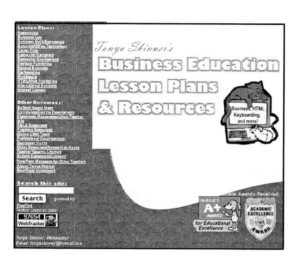

Computer Skills Lesson Plans

http://www.dpi.state.nc.us/Curriculum/
Computer.skills/lssnplns/CompCurr.LP.html

Computer Skills Lesson Plans, provided by the North Carolina Department of Public Instruction, features a series of lesson plans to help North Carolina teachers implement the state's computer skills curriculum. There is at least one lesson for each measure in the computer skills curriculum, as well as links to other curriculum areas.

Lesson Plans and Activities Technology

http://www.mcrel.org/resources/links/
techlessons.asp

Lesson Plans and Activities Technology is provided by the Mid-continent Regional Educational Laboratory (McREL), a nonprofit organization dedicated to improving the quality of education for all students. The site features 19 plans and ideas for integrating technology and the Internet into the K–12 classroom.

Sample Internet Lesson Plans and Learning Projects

http://www.schoolnet.ca/aboriginal/lessons/

Sample Internet Lesson Plans and Learning Projects presents lesson plans developed by Abenaki Associates. The plans are designed to (1) teach something about the Internet, (2) teach how to use the Internet, and (3) teach something by using information gained from the Internet. Many of the lessons are adaptable to the age group of the students in your classroom. Other lessons will be more suitable for experienced Internet users.

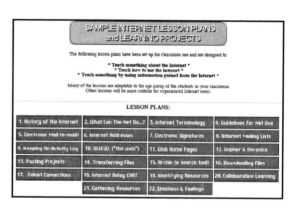

Wired Learning: Web-Based Lessons, Activites, & More

http://www.kn.pacbell.com/wired/wiredApps.html

Wired Learning: Web-Based Lessons, Activities, & More, provided by Pacific Bell, features activities, projects, resources, and tools to infuse technology in the K–12 classroom.

America's Job Bank

http://www.ajb.dni.us

America's Job Bank links 1,800 state employment offices across the country and lists 250,000 jobs.

Community Learning Network

http://www.cln.org/cln.html

Community Learning Network, is intended to help the K–12 teacher integrate the Internet into the classroom in all curriculum areas. Teachers and students can "Ask the Expert" specific questions and receive replies, get background information and teaching tips, and find links to Internet keypal exchanges and Internet projects.

Computers in Elementary Education

http://nimbus.temple.edu/~jallis00/

Computers in Elementary Education was designed by Jane Allison for the elementary school computer teacher, who may be called upon to teach a computer class, maintain a computer lab, or provide guidance to other teachers. The site provides links to educational sites, lesson plans, and ideas for using computers in the K–8 curriculum.

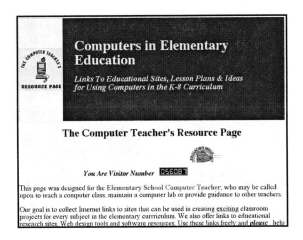

EdTech News

http://www.kn.pacbell.com/wired/news/news.html

EdTech News provides teachers, administrators, and librarians with resources for keeping up with current trends in educational technology.

Educational Standards and Curriculum Frameworks for Occupational/Business Education

http://PutnamValleySchools.org/StSu/OccEd.html

Educational Standards and Curriculum Frameworks for Occupational/Business Education is an annotated list of Internet sites with K-12 educational standards and curriculum frameworks documents, maintained by Charles Hill and the Putnam Valley Schools in New York.

Educational Standards and Curriculum Frameworks for: Technology

http://PutnamValleySchools.org/StSu/Technology.html

Educational Standards and Curriculum Frameworks for Technology is an annotated list of Internet sites with K-12 educational standards and curriculum frameworks documents, maintained by Charles Hill and the Putnam Valley Schools in New York.

Filamentality

http://www.kn.pacbell.com/wired/fil/

Filamentality is a fill-in-the-blank interactive Web site that guides teachers through picking a topic, searching the Web, gathering good Internet sites, and turning Web resources into activities appropriate for students. Filamenality has tips and help pages to hold a teacher's hand through the process. Teachers can even use Filamentality if they're newcomers to the Web.

Florida School-to-Work Information Navigator

http://www.flstw.fsu.edu/

Florida School-to-Work Information Navigator provides a variety of school-to-work resources. You can find links to grants and legislation, organizations and contacts, and work/labor employment. You can also subscribe to a mailing list.

International Technology Education Association

http://www.iteawww.org/

International Technology Education Association (ITEA) contains a variety of information on technology education, including links to several states' technology Web sites. Click Technology Education Resources and then K-12 sites for links to elementary schools, middle schools, and high schools that have technology education home pages.

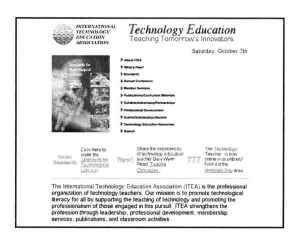

Internet in the One-Computer Classroom

http://members.aol.com/maestro12/web/class.html

Internet in the One-Computer Classroom describes activities that can be performed with an Internet connection in the classroom or at another location. For many Internet activities, the connection can be made at a remote site and resources brought to and from the classroom.

Job Options

http://www.joboptions.com/esp/plsql/espan_enter.espan_home

Job Options features a job and employer search engine as well as facilities for creating and posting resumes online. The site makers also permit a student to sign up, and they'll search a jobs database and e-mail any new openings that match the student's interests.

Journal of Industrial Teacher Education

http://scholar.lib.vt.edu/ejournals/JITE/jite.html

Journal of Industrial Teacher Education is an online journal for vocational education teachers.

New York State Education Department—Workforce Preparation and Continuing Education

http://www.nysed.gov/workforce/

New York State Education Department—Workforce Preparation and Continuing Education provides vocational and technology education teachers with links to resources, including Curriculum and Teaching, School Improvement, and Journals and Organizations.

Technology Student Association

http://www.tsawww.org/

Technology Student Association (TSA) is an organization for elementary school, middle school, and high school students interested in technology education. It includes information on competitions and conferences, on publications and supplies and offers links to other technology related Web sites. Students can also view recent issues of *School Scene* published by TSA.

WWW 4 Teachers

http://www.4teachers.org/home/index.shtml

WWW 4 Teachers is designed for teachers powering learning with technology. There is a how-to information system on technology for educators, Web lessons ready-to-go, new ideas, activities, and resources by teachers, and a Kids Speak section where students tell what they are doing with technology in the classroom.

Appendix 1:
Newsgroups (USENET) and Mailing Lists (Listservs)

Deja News

http://www.deja.com/

Deja News is a search engine dedicated to Internet discussion newsgroups. Type in a specific question or topic and the search engine will find the date, newsgroup, subject, and the author. The search has four levels: standard, adult, complete, and jobs.

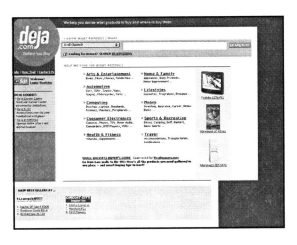

EdWeb

http://edweb.gsn.org/

EdWeb offers a collection of the best online educational resources available for K–12 students. These resources include newsgroups (public messages posted for everyone to see), listserv discussion groups (these are like private newsletters; you subscribe to a topic and then receive the latest news and views by e-mail) and electronic journals. To get to these groups, click Home Room at the bottom of the page, scroll down, and click Educational Resource Guide.

When you reach the EdWeb K–12 Resource Guide, click USENET News Group for lists of more than three dozen newsgroups for teachers and children. The newsgroups focus on every subject in the K–12 curriculum, including art, business education, health and physical education, math, music, social studies, and many others. You can read what other teachers think and, if you wish, write messages of your own. You can click Listserv Discussion Groups and E-Journals to find a long list of education-centered private newsletters (mailing lists) to which you can subscribe. There is a mailing list for just about every topic of interest to K–12 educators.

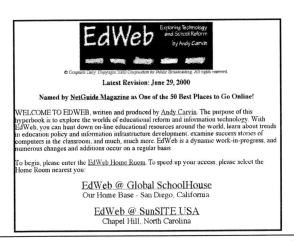

Appendix 2:
Search Tools

All-in-One Search Page

http://www.allonesearch.com/

All-in-One Search Page features a compilation of various search tools to help you find things on the Internet. For example, scroll down the page and click World Wide Web. There, you will find AltaVista Web Search, InfoSeek, Lycos, WebCrawler, Yahoo!, and other search tools. Just enter key-words, and your search of the Web begins. If you want to find tools to search for someone's e-mail address, return to the Home Page and click People. If you are interested in software, click Software to search for useful programs you can download. If you want to find USENET Newsgroups, click General Internet.

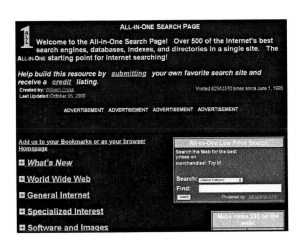

Inference Find

http://www.infind.com/

Inference Find is a fast search engine that elimi-nates duplicates while organizing results. Not only does it search across several search engines (AltaVista, Excite, InfoSeek, Lycos, WebCrawler, and Yahoo!), but it can also be configured to search any search engine.

BigHub.com

http://www.isleuth.com/

BigHub.com, formerly known as iSleuth.com, is ranked by the *New York Times* and *Miami Herald* as one of the top 10 search engines on the Web. This search engine lets you search multiple engines, news, Web databases simultaneously to receive a summary of results.

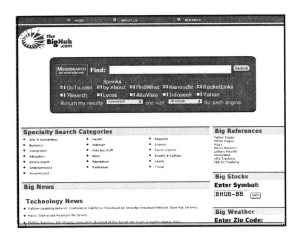

The Internet Sleuth

http://www.isleuth.com/

The Internet Sleuth provides you with quick keyword searches of more than 1,000 searchable databases on the Internet. Enter a keyword in Lycos, InfoSeek, AltaVista, Yahoo!, or Deja News to find lists of Internet sites that may contain the requested information. You can also search the Internet Sleuth by category, for example, Education, Math, or Science.

Google

http://www.google.com

Google is a very fast and comprehensive search
engine that indexes more than 1 billion Web pages.

Appendix 3:
Evaluation Forms

✏️ Educational Web Sites Recommended by Others

✏️ Educational Web Sites You Discover

Educational Web Sites Recommended by Others

Use this form to record and supplement information on educational Web sites described in this book or recommended to you by others. The form allows you to collect Web site information that is more detailed than the information you may have originally been given, and can be used to evaluate the site's usefulness in terms of your own particular needs.

Site Name: _____ Site Address/URL: _____

Brief Description: _____

_____

This site was recommended by: _____

For: _____

I could use this site for the following:

❑ Reference source for my students (appropriate reading level and content)
❑ Source of up-to-date data for analysis by my students
❑ Source of project(s) for my classes to join
❑ Source of connections to other projects at other sites
❑ Question/answer site where students can have their questions answered
❑ Ask-an-Expert sessions (special sessions to interact with a writer or other expert)
❑ Interactive sessions (students interact with the site's learning activity while online)
❑ Reference for myself (content for my subject area, lesson plans, etc.)
❑ Newsgroup site where I can share and get information
❑ Professional information site (educational research or other relevant material)
❑ Other: _____

Educational Setting—Mark all that apply: K 1 2 3 4 5 6 7 8 9 10 11 12 T

❑ Individual students   ❑ Downloadable content   ❑ Completely interactive
❑ Student groups   ❑ Interactive time necessary

Subject Areas—Check all that apply:

❑ Language Arts   ❑ Social Studies   ❑ Science
❑ Mathematics   ❑ Arts   ❑ Foreign Language
❑ Careers   ❑ Business   ❑ Cross-Curricular

Rate the site performance for each criterion listed.

	Exemplary	Adequate	Unacceptable
Content			
Does the content meet my needs?	❑	❑	❑
Educational Value			
Can students collaborate with other sites?	❑	❑	❑
Can teachers share results?	❑	❑	❑
Does the site respond to student questions?	❑	❑	❑
Technical Quality			
Is the site easy for my students to navigate?	❑	❑	❑
OVERALL RATING	❑	❑	❑

Educational Web Sites You Discover

Use this form to record complete information on educational Web sites you discover as you explore the World Wide Web. The information can be used to help you evaluate the site's usefulness in terms of your own particular needs.

Site Name: _____ Site Address/URL: _____

Brief Description: _____

_____

Approximate time necessary to access and download desired information: _____

Check all the categories that describe the site:

❏ Student Reference   ❏ Question/Answer   ❏ Newsgroup
❏ Data Source   ❏ Access to an Expert   ❏ Professional Information
❏ Student Projects   ❏ Interactive   ❏ Other _____
❏ Connections to Other Projects   ❏ Teacher Reference

Educational Setting—Mark all that apply: K 1 2 3 4 5 6 7 8 9 10 11 12 T

❏ Individual students   ❏ Downloadable content   ❏ Completely interactive
❏ Student groups   ❏ Interactive time necessary

Subject Areas—Check all that apply:

❏ Language Arts   ❏ Social Studies   ❏ Science
❏ Mathematics   ❏ Arts   ❏ Foreign Language
❏ Careers   ❏ Business   ❏ Cross-Curricular

Rate the site performance for each criterion listed.

	Exemplary	Adequate	Unacceptable
Content			
1. Is it correct, accurate?	❏	❏	❏
2. Is it from an authoritative source?	❏	❏	❏
3. Is it free from stereotypes and bias?	❏	❏	❏
4. Is this the best medium for this information?	❏	❏	❏
5. Do the images enhance the content?	❏	❏	❏
Educational Value			
1. Is the information useful?	❏	❏	❏
2. Is the information readable by students?	❏	❏	❏
3. Is the information available elsewhere?	❏	❏	❏
4. Can students collaborate with other sites?	❏	❏	❏
5. Can teachers share results?	❏	❏	❏
6. Does the site respond to student questions?	❏	❏	❏
Technical Quality			
1. Does the site work the way it is intended to work?	❏	❏	❏
2. Are all the links current?	❏	❏	❏
3. Is the home page concise and quick to view?	❏	❏	❏
4. Are lengthy pictures files saved for later pages?	❏	❏	❏
5. Is the menu clear, informative, and current?	❏	❏	❏
6. Is the navigation for the site obvious?	❏	❏	❏
OVERALL RATING	❏	❏	❏

Appendix 4

ISTE National Educational Technology Standards (NETS) and Performance Indicators for Teachers

All classroom teachers should be prepared to meet the following standards and performance indicators.

I. Technology Operations and Concepts
Teachers demonstrate a sound understanding of technology operations and concepts. Teachers:
A. demonstrate introductory knowledge, skills, and understanding of concepts related to technology (as described in the ISTE National Educational Technology Standards for Students).
B. demonstrate continual growth in technology knowledge and skills to stay abreast of current and emerging technologies.

II. Planning and Designing Learning Environments and Experiences
Teachers plan and design effective learning environments and experiences supported by technology. Teachers:
A. design developmentally appropriate learning opportunities that apply technology-enhanced instructional strategies to support the diverse needs of learners.
B. apply current research on teaching and learning with technology when planning learning environments and experiences.
C. identify and locate technology resources and evaluate them for accuracy and suitability.
D. plan for the management of technology resources within the context of learning activities.
E. plan strategies to manage student learning in a technology-enhanced environment.

III. Teaching, Learning, and the Curriculum
Teachers implement curriculum plans that include methods and strategies for applying technology to maximize student learning. Teachers:
A. facilitate technology-enhanced experiences that address content standards and student technology standards.
B. use technology to support learner-centered strategies that address the diverse needs of students.
C. apply technology to develop students' higher-order skills and creativity.
D. manage student learning activities in a technology-enhanced environment.

IV. Assessment and Evaluation
Teachers apply technology to facilitate a variety of effective assessment and evaluation strategies. Teachers:
A. apply technology in assessing student learning of subject matter using a variety of assessment techniques.
B. use technology resources to collect and analyze data, interpret results, and communicate findings to improve instructional practice and maximize student learning.
C. apply multiple methods of evaluation to determine students' appropriate use of technology resources for learning, communication, and productivity.

V. Productivity and Professional Practice
Teachers use technology to enhance their productivity and professional practice. Teachers:
A. use technology resources to engage in ongoing professional development and lifelong learning.
B. continually evaluate and reflect on professional practice to make informed decisions regarding the use of technology in support of student learning.
C. apply technology to increase productivity.
D. use technology to communicate and collaborate with peers, parents, and the larger community in order to nurture student learning.

VI. Social, Ethical, Legal, and Human Issues
Teachers understand the social, ethical, legal, and human issues surrounding the use of technology in PK-12 schools and apply that understanding in practice. Teachers:
A. model and teach legal and ethical practice related to technology use.
B. apply technology resources to enable and empower learners with diverse backgrounds, characteristics, and abilities.
C. identify and use technology resources that affirm diversity.
D. promote safe and healthy use of technology resources.
E. facilitate equitable access to technology resources for all students.

Index